The Open University

Mathematics Foundation Course Unit 34

NUMBER SYSTEMS

Prepared by the Mathematics Foundation Course Team

Correspondence Text 34

The Open University Press

Open University courses provide a method of study for independent learners through an integrated teaching system including textual material, radio and television programmes and short residential courses. This text is one of a series that make up the correspondence element of the Mathematics Foundation Course.

The Open University's courses represent a new system of university level education. Much of the teaching material is still in a developmental stage. Courses and course materials are, therefore, kept continually under revision. It is intended to issue regular up-dating notes as and when the need arises, and new editions will be brought out when necessary.

Further information on Open University courses may be obtained from The Admissions Office, The Open University, P.O. Box 48, Bletchley, Buckinghamshire.

The Open University Press
Walton Hall, Bletchley, Bucks

First Published 1971
Copyright © 1971 The Open University

Printed in Great Britain by
J W Arrowsmith Ltd, Bristol 3

SBN 335 01033 4

Contents

Objectives

The principal aim of this unit is to construct the set of integers, Z, the set of rational numbers, Q, and the set of real numbers, R, from the natural number system, and to justify some of the properties of the number systems used in earlier units.

After working through this unit you should be able to:

(i) represent a natural number using a given base;

(ii) explain how the integers are constructed from the natural numbers;

(iii) find the highest common factor of two positive integers, using the Euclidean algorithm;

(iv) state the existence theorem given on page 26, understand its importance, and use it in simple applications;

(v) state the Fundamental Theorem of Arithmetic;

(vi) explain how the rational numbers are constructed from the integers;

(vii) understand how the real numbers are constructed from the rationals;

(viii) represent real numbers in terms of continued fractions and decimals;

(ix) set up a one-one correspondence between N and Q^+, and show that no such correspondence exists between N and R^+.

Note

Before working through this correspondence text, make sure you have read the general introduction to the mathematics course in the Study Guide, as this explains the philosophy underlying the whole course. You should also be familiar with the section which explains how a text is constructed and the meanings attached to the stars and other symbols in the margin, as this will help you to find your way through the text.

Structural Diagram

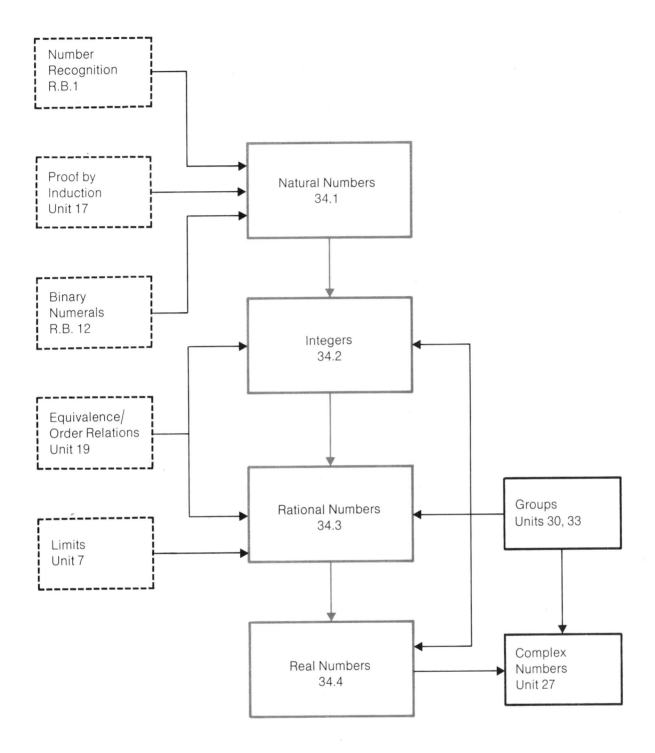

Glossary Page

Terms which are defined in this glossary are printed in CAPITALS.

COMMON FACTOR — A COMMON FACTOR of two or more given INTEGERS is an integer which is a FACTOR of each of the given integers.   21

CONTINUED FRACTION — A simple CONTINUED FRACTION is an expression of the form   44

$$a_0 + \cfrac{1}{a_1 + \cfrac{1}{a_2 + \cfrac{1}{a_3 + \cdots}}}$$

In the text, the a's are POSITIVE INTEGERS, except for a_0, which is zero in some cases.

CO-PRIME — Two INTEGERS are CO-PRIME if their h.c.f. is 1.   21

DIVIDE — The INTEGER b DIVIDES the integer a if there is an integer c such that $a = bc \neq 0$.   19

DIVISOR — See FACTOR.

EQUALLY NUMEROUS — In the text, two sets are said to be EQUALLY NUMEROUS if it is possible to set up a one-one correspondence (a matching) between the elements of one set and the elements of the other.   49

EUCLIDEAN ALGORITHM — The EUCLIDEAN ALGORITHM is a systematic arithmetical procedure for finding the h.c.f. of two (positive) INTEGERS in a finite number of steps.   21

FACTOR — The INTEGER b is a FACTOR (or DIVISOR) of the integer a if there is an integer c such that   19

$$a = bc \neq 0.$$

GREATEST LOWER BOUND (g.l.b.) — The GREATEST LOWER BOUND (g.l.b.) of a subset S of a set of numbers P, with order relation $\leqslant$, is the LOWER BOUND l_g, such that   5

$$l_g \in P \quad \text{and} \quad l \leqslant l_g$$

for every lower bound l of S.

HIGHEST COMMON FACTOR (h.c.f.) — The HIGHEST COMMON FACTOR (h.c.f.) of two given INTEGERS is the largest (positive) common FACTOR of the given integers.   21

INTEGER — An INTEGER is an equivalence class of the set of number pairs defined by the relation ρ_1:   10

$$(m, n)\rho_1(m', n')$$

if and only if

$$m + n' = n + m'.$$

INTEGER PAIR — An INTEGER PAIR is an ordered pair of INTEGERS (m, n), where m is any integer and n is any integer except zero.   31

| LEAST UPPER BOUND (l.u.b.) | The LEAST UPPER BOUND (l.u.b.) of a subset S of a set of numbers P, with order relation $\leqslant$, is the UPPER BOUND u_l such that $$u_l \in P \quad \text{and} \quad u_l \leqslant u$$ for every upper bound u of S. | 39 |

Notation

It is a mathematical fact of life that we are obliged to use the same notation for different things. As with other facts of life, this is something we learn to cope with as we grow more mature. In this text this fact of life rears its ugly head. Thus, in general, we use (m, n) to denote an ordered pair of elements from some particular set. However, we also use (m, n) to denote the highest common factor of the integers m and n. We use $+$ for the operation of addition of natural numbers, the operation of addition of integers, and so on; strictly speaking, these operations are different, but, because they all have similar properties, it would be silly to use a different symbol for each of them.

We hope that by now you are sufficiently mathematically mature to be able to interpret the notation correctly in any particular context.

The following symbols appear in the text:

N	The set of natural numbers.
Z	The set of integers.
Z^+	The set of positive integers.
Z^-	The set of negative integers.
Q	The set of rational numbers.
Q^+	The set of positive rationals.
Q^-	The set of negative rationals.
R	The set of real numbers.
R^+	The set of positive real numbers.
R^-	The set of negative real numbers.
$a\|b$	The integer a divides the integer b.
$\mathscr{L}, \mathscr{R}$	The Left- and Right-hand classes respectively in a partition of the rationals.
$a_0 + \dfrac{1}{a_1 +} \dfrac{1}{a_2 +} \cdots$	A continued fraction.
$\aleph_0$	Aleph nought — the transfinite number associated with the set N.
c	The transfinite number associated with the set R.

Bibliography

T. Dantzig, *Number, the Language of Science*, 4th ed. (Allen & Unwin, 1962).

This is a very readable book devoted to the subject of number, and containing an unusually interesting historical chapter. The scope of the book is just about right for the unit, though the treatment is not always complete in a technical sense.

W. J. LeVeque, *Elementary Theory of Numbers* (Addison-Wesley, 1956).

This book will tell you more about the theory of natural numbers, but not enough to swamp and depress you. It contains standard topics such as the Euclidean Algorithm, the Unique Factorization Theorem and continued fractions, and in addition contains a fair amount of modular arithmetic (i.e. congruences), and some results in Diophantine equations.

N. Y. Vilenkin, *Stories about Sets* (Academic Press, 1968).

If you want to read more about transfinite numbers and related topics, this is an excellent book to get.

F. M. Hall, *An Introduction to Abstract Algebra*, Vol. I (Cambridge University Press, 1966).

This book gives a straightforward, rather brief treatment of the number systems considered in this text. The relevant chapters are Chapters 4 and 5.

Ah! why, ye Gods, should two and two make four?

Alexander Pope
The Dunciad, Bk. 2

34.0 INTRODUCTION

In this unit we are concerned with number systems. We have referred to number systems in all the earlier units, so in a sense this unit provides a link between the material studied so far and *Unit 36, Mathematical Structures.*

We begin by discussing the system of natural (counting) numbers, which came first historically. A rigorous definition of the natural numbers requires a great deal of care: it is a problem of logic rather than mathematics. In this unit we do not propose to discuss the definition of the natural numbers in terms of the more basic concepts of sets and relations: instead we shall take the natural numbers and their properties for granted.

Once we accept the natural number system, we can go ahead and rigorously define the system of integers, the rational number system, the real number system and the complex number system. We successively "build" each system from its predecessor, and the systems grow "richer" as we proceed.

This approach is summed up in the words of Kronecker:

God made integers, all else is the work of man.*

We shall discuss the system of integers, the rational number system and the real number system in detail. We also devote a section of this text to some ideas about *transfinite numbers.* We shall say very little about the complex number system in this text as this system has already been discussed in *Units 27* and *29.*

---

* *Jahresberichte der Deutschen Mathematiker Vereinigung, Bd. 2, page 19.*

34.1 THE NATURAL NUMBERS

34.1.0 Introduction

The natural numbers 1, 2, 3, 4, 5, ... arose historically as counting devices. By means of them one could say how many cattle a tribesman owned or how many wives King Solomon ran.

Such physical situations gave birth to implicit operations of addition and multiplication of "counting" numbers.

> If a tribesman owning m oxen buys n more,
> how many does he then have?
> If one ox is equivalent to x sheep, what are y oxen equivalent to?

In time, people were able to think of natural numbers divorced from any immediate physical situation. "Equations" such as

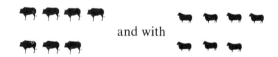

showed that the nature of number does not depend on the natures of sheep or oxen. The symbol 7 was associated with

and with

and so on, and the above equations were each replaced by

$$5 + 2 = 7.$$

We can go a little further than this. Arising from the physical situations, the operations of addition and multiplication of natural numbers have implicit properties.

Exercise 1

 (i) What is the answer to the first question in the text?
(ii) What is the answer to the second question in the text?
(iii) In (i), what is the sheep equivalent of the tribesman's herd after the transaction? Work this out by two different methods, and so obtain an identity. ∎

We know that

> $m + n$ sheep is the same as $n + m$ sheep,

i.e.

> $m + n = n + m,$

and we see from Exercise 1 that

$x(m + n)$ sheep is the same as $xm + xn$ sheep.

i.e.

$$x(m + n) = xm + xn.$$

This sort of arithmetic of the "counting" numbers proved adequate for man's needs for many thousands of years. However, the Greek mathematicians were interested in number for its own sake and not just as a trading tool. Aeschylus wrote:

> Number, the inducer of philosophies,
> The synthesis of letters...*

and Plato wrote:

> Arithmetic has a very great and elevating effect, compelling the soul to reason about abstract number, and if visible or tangible objects are obtruding upon the argument, refusing to be satisfied.†

---

* Quoted in Thomson, J. A., *Introduction to Science*, chap. 1 (London).
† *Republic*, Jowett, Bk. 7, p. 525.

Solution 1

  (i) $m + n$ oxen.

 (ii) xy sheep.

(iii) Before the transaction, the tribesman has the equivalent of xm sheep.

In the transaction he obtains the equivalent of xn sheep.

Therefore he finishes with the equivalent of $xm + xn$ sheep.

But his final herd consists of $m + n$ oxen; therefore it is equivalent to $x(m + n)$ sheep. Therefore $x(m + n)$ sheep $= xm + xn$ sheep. ∎

34.1.1 The Natural Number System

The definition of the natural number system raises problems of logic and philosophy. We have already mentioned some of these problems at the foundations of mathematics in *Unit 17, Logic II*, section 17.1.2.

In this unit we shall take the natural number system for granted.

We have the set N comprising

$$1, 2, 3, \ldots$$

together with two binary operations $+$ and $\times$ defined on it.

The natural number system has the following properties.

 (i) The set of natural numbers is closed under $+$ and $\times$. (We write $a \times b$ as ab, etc.)

(ii) For all $a, b, c \in N$,

$$\left. \begin{aligned} a + b &= b + a \\ ab &= ba \end{aligned} \right\} \text{\textit{commutative property}}$$

$$\left. \begin{aligned} a + (b + c) &= (a + b) + c \\ a(bc) &= (ab)c \end{aligned} \right\} \text{\textit{associative property}}$$

$$a(b + c) = ab + ac \qquad \textit{distributive property.}$$

(iii) The natural number 1 has the property that, for every natural number a,

$$1a = a1 = a;$$

that is, 1 is an *identity element* for multiplication.

(iv) If

$$m + k = n + k,$$

then

$$m = n,$$

where m, n and k are any natural numbers.

If

$$mk = nk,$$

then

$$m = n,$$

where m, n and k are any natural numbers.

These are *cancellation* properties.

There is a further property of the natural numbers which we discussed in *Unit 17** — the axiom of mathematical induction:

Given that S is a subset of N, if

(1) $1 \in S$

and

(2) $k + 1 \in S$ whenever $k \in S$,

then $S = N$.

We have seen in many units that proof by mathematical induction has an important place in mathematics.

There is another important property of the natural number system. In *Unit 19, Relations* we defined an order relation on a set A to be a relation on A which is reflexive, anti-symmetric and transitive.

We define the relation $<$ on N by

Definition 1
* * *

$$a < b$$

if and only if there is an element c such that

$$b = a + c$$

where $a, b, c \in N$.

If $a < b$, we say "a is less than b" or "b is greater than a".

We define the relation $\leqslant$ on N by

Definition 2
* * *

$$a \leqslant b$$

if and only if *either $a < b$ or $a = b$.*

Exercise 1

Exercise 1
(2 minutes)

Show that the relation $\leqslant$ on N is an order relation. ■

We see from Exercise 1 that $\leqslant$ is an order relation on N, and we can write

Main Text
* *

$$1 \leqslant 2 \leqslant 3 \leqslant 4 \leqslant \cdots.$$

Also, we know that

$$2 = 1 + 1$$
$$3 = 2 + 1$$
$$4 = 3 + 1$$
$$\cdots$$

This enables us to represent the natural numbers by equally spaced points on a "number line":

If $a < b$, then a occurs to the left of b on the line.

The relation $\leqslant$ has a further, very important property: if S is any non-empty subset of N, then S has a greatest lower bound which belongs to S (a least member). That is, there is a natural number $l_g \in S$ such that

$$l_g \leqslant s$$

for each $s \in S$.

---

* In *Unit 17* we identified N with the set of positive integers Z^+. The axiom of mathematical induction is really a property of N; however, in section 34.2 we shall show that N and Z^+ are isomorphic for addition.

Solution 1

(i) $a = a$, so

$$a \leqslant a,$$

i.e.

$\leqslant$ is reflexive.

(ii) $\leqslant$ is anti-symmetric if, whenever $a \leqslant b$ and $b \leqslant a$, then $a = b$.

From the definition, it follows that

$$a \leqslant b \quad \text{and} \quad b < a$$

never hold simultaneously, and, if $a \leqslant b$ and $b = a$, then $a = b$,

i.e. $\leqslant$ is anti-symmetric.

(iii) If $a, b, d \in N$ and

$$a < b \quad \text{and} \quad b < d,$$

there are elements $c, e \in N$ such that

$$b = a + c$$
$$d = b + e.$$

Hence

$$d = a + (c + e)$$

i.e.

$$d = a + f$$

where

$$f = c + e \in N,$$

and so

$$a < d,$$

i.e. $<$ is transitive.

If $a = b$ and $b < d$, then $a < d$.

If $a < b$ and $b = d$, then $a < d$.

If $a = b$ and $b = c$, then $a = c$.

Hence, if $a \leqslant b$ and $b \leqslant d$, then $a \leqslant d$,

i.e. $\leqslant$ is transitive.

It follows that $\leqslant$ is an order relation on N.

34.1.2 Representation of Natural Numbers

We usually represent each of the natural numbers by a unique string made up of the digits $1, 2, \ldots, 9$. The next number after nine is called ten, followed by eleven, which we think of as ten plus one, followed by twelve, which is ten plus two, etc. It was a major development to start writing sequences of digits such as 11 to represent one ten plus one, 12 to represent one ten plus two, etc. Then 342 represents three ten-squared's plus four tens plus two. Ten is called the *base* of the representation. The following diagram shows the number 5306 represented on an abacus, using base ten.

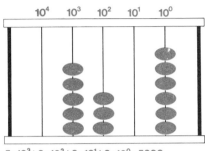

$$5 \times 10^3 + 3 \times 10^2 + 0 \times 10^1 + 6 \times 10^0 = 5306$$

Another way of representing numbers which has become familiar in modern times is the binary representation (using base two), by which each natural number is expressed as a sequence of 0's and 1's. Thus in binary notation 101 means

$$1 \times 2^2 + 0 \times 2^1 + 1 \times 2^0,$$

that is, the number 5 (in base ten). The natural number 57 (in base ten) expressed in binary notation is 111001.

Exercise 1

(i) Express the following numbers (which are given in base ten) in base two and base three:

$$5, 17, 24, 65.$$

(ii) Express 5 and 17 in base three, and multiply them together working with base three. ◼

Using different bases is not just an idle pastime. Computers use base two, and in some cases, base sixteen for sorting information. The Babylonians used a base of sixty, of which our 360 degrees, 60 seconds and 60 minutes is a carry-over; the Mayans used bases of twenty and fifty-two for astronomical calculations; and until recently British coinage was based on a combination of base ten (for digits) base twelve (for pennies) and base twenty (for shillings). For a long time there has been a Duo-decimal Society, advocating the use of base twelve.

Solution 1

Solution 1

(i) In the scale of 2,

> 5 is written as 101,
> 17 is written as 10001,
> 24 is written as 11000,
> 65 is written as 1000001.

In the scale of 3,

> 5 is written as 12,
> 17 is written as 122,
> 24 is written as 220,
> 65 is written as 2102,

(ii) carrying out the multiplication, we obtain:

$$
\begin{array}{r}
122 \\
12 \\
\hline
1021 \\
122 \\
\hline
10011 \\
\hline
\end{array}
$$

(continued from page 7)

Mayan Number Representation

Egyptian Number Representation

Early Greek Number Representation

It is also worth remarking in passing that zero is not considered to be a natural number, since it is a comparatively recent concept. The Indians are usually credited with first discussing it around the seventh century, although the Babylonians must have had some appreciation of it, and the Arabs are credited with introducing the symbol 0. The Mayan Indians of Central America also introduced a symbol for zero, at about the same time.

34.2   THE INTEGERS

34.2.0   Introduction

Natural numbers arose as counting devices. By their means you can say how many pounds you have in the bank. But suppose you have an overdraft of £20; how much have you got then? There is no natural number describing the amount you have, so on practical grounds it became necessary to concoct some new kind of number. You could say

> "the number of pounds I have is such that if I added 30 to it I would get 10".

But this still will not do, because there is no number (i.e. natural number — this is the only kind of number we have so far in our system) having this property. The equation

$$30 + x = 10$$

has no solution in N.

To provide a solution to equations of the form $m + x = n$, we have to extend our system, and we do this by defining new entities which we call *integers*.

34.2.1   Construction of the Integers

If m, n are natural numbers, we call the ordered pair (m, n) a *number pair*. That is, (m, n) is an element of the Cartesian product $N \times N$.

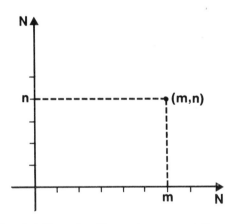

(Note that $0 \notin N$, so the N-axes intersect at the point $(1, 1)$.)

We now define a relation on the set of number pairs. How can we usefully define such a relation?

We note that, in the "money in the bank" context,

> having £25 in the bank and owing £10

is in a sense equivalent to

> having £50 in the bank and owing £35,

etc.

We define a relation ρ_1 on the set of number pairs by

$$(m, n)\rho_1(m', n')$$

if and only if

$$m + n' = m' + n.$$

(Note that this definition is given in terms of addition of natural numbers.)

One immediate conclusion is that $(m + x, n + x)\rho_1(m, n)$ for all x.

Exercise 1

Show that ρ_1 is an equivalence relation on the set of all ordered pairs of natural numbers. ■

Exercise 1
(1 minute)

As ρ_1 is an equivalence relation, it partitions the set of number pairs, i.e. $(N \times N)$, into *equivalence classes*. We define these equivalence classes to be integers.

Main Text
* * *

Definition 2
* * *

If we look at a pictorial representation of $N \times N$, we see that the equivalence class to which (m, n) belongs consists of all those elements of $N \times N$ which lie on the "diagonal" which passes through (m, n).

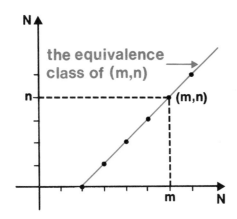

We know that any member of an equivalence class determines the whole equivalence class. We shall denote the class to which (m, n) belongs by $[(m, n)]$.

Notation 1
* * *

The classes $[(m, n)]$, $[(m', n')]$ will be the same if

$$(m, n)\rho_1(m', n');$$

in this case we write

$$[(m, n)] = [(m', n')].$$

Definition 3
* * *

34.2.2   Addition and Multiplication of Integers

Addition

We define the operation of addition on the set of number pairs by

$$(m_1, n_1) + (m_2, n_2) = (m_1 + m_2, n_1 + n_2).$$

In *Unit 19, Relations*, we defined an equivalence relation ρ, and a binary operation $\circ$, both defined on a set A, to be *compatible* if and only if

$$(x_1 \circ y_1) \, \rho \, (x_2 \circ y_2)$$

whenever

$$x_1 \, \rho \, x_2 \quad \text{and} \quad y_1 \, \rho \, y_2$$

$(x_1, x_2, y_1, y_2 \in A)$.

We shall show that the operation of addition of number pairs is compatible with the relation ρ_1.
Suppose

$$(m_1, n_1)\rho_1(m_1', n_1') \quad \text{and} \quad (m_2, n_2)\rho_1(m_2', n_2').$$

Then

$$m_1 + n_1' = m_1' + n_1$$
$$m_2 + n_2' = m_2' + n_2,$$

so

$$(m_1 + m_2) + (n_1' + n_2') = (m_1' + m_2') + (n_1 + n_2),$$

hence

$$(m_1 + m_2, n_1 + n_2)\rho_1(m_1' + m_2', n_1' + n_2'),$$

that is,

$$\big((m_1, n_1) + (m_2, n_2)\big)\rho_1\big((m_1', n_1') + (m_2', n_2')\big) ;$$

that is,

$+$ is compatible with ρ_1.

We have the following commutative diagram.

$$(m_1, n_1), (m_2, n_2) \xrightarrow{\quad + \quad} (m_1 + m_2, n_1 + n_2)$$

$$\rho_1 \Big\downarrow \qquad\qquad\qquad\qquad \Big\downarrow \rho_1$$

$$(m_1', n_1'), (m_2', n_2') \xrightarrow{\quad + \quad} (m_1' + m_2', n_1' + n_2')$$

We see that the operation of addition of number pairs defines an operation of addition of integers:

$$[(m_1, n_1)] + [(m_2, n_2)] = [(m_1 + m_2, n_1 + n_2)].$$

We denote both the addition operations by $+$.

It follows that addition of integers has the following properties:

  $+$ is a closed binary operation on the set of integers;
  $+$ is commutative;
  $+$ is associative.

These properties follow immediately from the properties of addition on N.

Further, if

$$[(m, n)] + [(x, y)] = [(m', n')] + [(x, y)],$$

then

$$[(m, n)] = [(m', n')].$$

(*continued on page 12*)

Solution 34.2.1.1

Solution 34.2.1.1

(i)
$$m + n = m + n,$$

so

$$(m, n)\rho_1(m, n),$$

i.e. ρ_1 is reflexive.

(ii) If $(m, n)\rho_1(m', n')$, then

$$m + n' = m' + n,$$

so

$$m' + n = m + n',$$

i.e. ρ_1 is symmetric.

(iii) If $(m, n)\rho_1(m', n')$ and $(m', n')\rho_1(m'', n'')$, then

$$m + n' = m' + n$$

and

$$m' + n'' = m'' + n'.$$

Adding the last two equations, and using the commutative and associative properties of $+$ on N, we obtain

$$m + n'' + (m' + n') = m'' + n + (m' + n').$$

By the cancellation property, it follows that

$$m + n'' = m'' + n,$$

i.e.

$$(m, n)\rho_1(m'', n''),$$

i.e. ρ_1 is transitive.

It follows that ρ_1 is an equivalence relation. ∎

(continued from page 11)

This *cancellation property* follows from the cancellation property of natural numbers. (See Exercise 1 (i).)

Exercise 1

Exercise 1
(2 minutes)

(i) If

$$((m, n) + (x, y))\rho_1((m', n') + (x, y)),$$

show that

$$(m, n)\rho_1(m', n').$$

(ii) Find

$$[(m, n)] + [(x, x)].$$

(iii) Find

$$[(m, n)] + [(m' + n, m + n')]. \quad ∎$$

Exercise 2

Exercise 2
(1 minute)

Solve

(i) $[(6, 5)] + [(x, y)] = [(6, 5)].$

(ii) $[(6, 5)] + [(x, y)] = [(1, 4)]. \quad ∎$

Zero

In Exercise 1 (ii), we found that

$$[(m, n)] + [(x, x)] = [(m, n)].$$

Since addition of integers is commutative, we also have

$$[(x, x)] + [(m, n)] = [(m, n)].$$

That is, $[(x, x)]$ is an *identity element* for addition of integers. The additive identity element is in fact *unique*. (See *Unit 30, Groups I.*)

The integer $[(x, x)]$ is called zero.

Subtraction

We define the operation of *subtraction* on the set of integers by

$$[(m, n)] - [(m', n')] = [(x, y)]$$

if and only if

$$[(m, n)] = [(x, y)] + [(m', n')].$$

We denote an integer of the form

$$[(x, x)] - [(m, n)]$$

by

$$-[(m, n)]$$

Thus

$$[(m, n)] + (-[(m, n)]) = [(x, x)];$$

that is,

$$-[(m, n)] \text{ is an } additive\ inverse\ of\ [(m, n)];$$

it is in fact unique. (See *Unit 30, Groups I.*)

The equation

$$[(m', n')] + [(x, y)] = [(m, n)]$$

has the *unique* solution

$$[(x, y)] = [(m, n)] + (-[(m', n')]).$$

Summary

  (i) $+$ is a closed binary operation on the set Z;
(ii) $+$ is associative;
(iii) $[(x, x)]$ is an *additive identity* in Z;
(iv) the *additive inverse* of $[(m, n)]$ is $-[(m, n)]$.

It follows that

$$(Z, +) \text{ is a } group.$$

We also know that

  (v) $+$ is commutative,

so

$$(Z, +) \text{ is an Abelian group.}$$

(*continued on page 15*)

Solution 1 Solution 1

(i) If

$$(m + x, n + y)\rho_1(m' + x, n' + y),$$

then

$$m + x + n' + y = m' + x + n + y.$$

By the cancellation property of natural numbers, we have

$$m + n' = m' + n$$

so

$$(m, n)\rho_1(m', n').$$

(ii) $$[(m, n)] + [(x, x)] = [(m + x, n + x)].$$

But

$$(m + x, n + x)\rho_1(m, n),$$

hence

$$[(m, n)] + [(x, x)] = [(m, n)].$$

(iii) $$[(m, n)] + [(m' + n, m + n')] = [(m + m' + n, n + m + n')]$$
$$= [(m', n')] + [(m + n, m + n)]$$
$$= [(m', n')] \quad \text{by (ii).} \qquad \blacksquare$$

Solution 2 Solution 2

(i) We require

$$[(6 + x, 5 + y)] = [(6, 5)],$$

i.e.

$$(6 + x, 5 + y)\rho_1(6, 5),$$

i.e.

$$6 + x + 5 = 6 + y + 5$$

So

$$[(x, y)] = [(n, n)],$$

where n is any natural number.

(ii) We require

$$[(6 + x, 5 + y)] = [(1, 4)],$$

i.e.,

$$(6 + x, 5 + y)\rho_1(1, 4)$$

i.e.,

$$6 + x + 4 = 5 + y + 1$$

i.e.,

$$10 + x = 6 + y.$$

Thus

$$[(x, y)] = [(n, n + 4)],$$

where n is any natural number. $\qquad \blacksquare$

Multiplication

We have given a full discussion of the addition of integers and its properties. We define multiplication on the set of integers similarly. For multiplication we shall omit the chores and list the important stages in the development.

(i) We define *multiplication* of number pairs by

$$(m_1, n_1) \times (m_2, n_2) = (m_1 m_2 + n_1 n_2, m_1 n_2 + m_2 n_1).$$

(ii) We can show that the operation defined in (i) is compatible with the equivalence relation ρ_1.

(iii) We define the operation of *multiplication* on the set of equivalence classes by

$$[(m_1, n_1)] \times [(m_2, n_2)] = [(m_1, n_1) \times (m_2, n_2)].$$

(iv) It follows that multiplication of integers has the following properties:

$\times$ is a closed binary operation on the set Z,
$\times$ is commutative;
$\times$ is associative.

These properties follow immediately from the properties of multiplication on N.

(v) We can show that if

$$[(m, n)] \times [(x, y)] = [(m, n)] \times [(x', y')],$$

where $[(m, n)]$ is not zero, then

$$[(x, y)] = [(x', y')]$$

i.e. we have a *cancellation rule* for multiplication.

(vi) $$[(m, n)] \times [(x, x)] = [(x, x)]$$

i.e. if we multiply any integer by zero we get zero.

(vii) $$[(m, n)] \times [(x + 1, x)] = [(m, n)].$$

Since multiplication of integers is commutative, we also have

$$[(x + 1, x)] \times [(m, n)] = [(m, n)].$$

That is, $[(x + 1, x)]$ is an *identity element* for multiplication of integers. The multiplicative identity element is unique.

(viii) If the equation

$$[(m, n)] \times [(x, y)] = [(m', n')]$$

has a solution, then the solution is unique.

Exercise 3

Exercise 3
(2 minutes)

Show that

(i) the equation

$$[(6, 3)] \times [(x, y)] = [(22, 10)]$$

has a *unique* solution in Z;

(ii) the equation

$$[(6, 3)] \times [(x, y)] = [(2, 1)]$$

has *no* solution in Z.   ∎

Solution 3 **Solution 3**

  (i) We require

$$[(6x + 3y, 3x + 6y)] = [(22, 10)],$$

    i.e.,

$$(6x + 3y, 3x + 6y)\rho_1(22, 10),$$

    i.e.,

$$6x + 3y + 10 = 3x + 6y + 22$$

    i.e.,

$$3x = 3y + 12$$

(by the cancellation rule for natural numbers). Thus

$$[(x, y)] = [(n + 4, n)],$$

where n is any natural number.

  (ii) We require

$$(6x + 3y, 3x + 6y)\rho_1(2, 1)$$

    i.e.,

$$6x + 3y + 1 = 3x + 6y + 2$$

    i.e.,

$$3x = 3y + 1$$

(by the cancellation rule for natural numbers).

There are no natural numbers x and y which satisfy this equation, so the given equation has *no* solution in Z. ∎

Summary

  (i) $\times$ is a closed binary operation on the set Z;

  (ii) $\times$ is associative.

    It follows that

$$(Z, \times) \text{ is a } semi\text{-}group.$$

    We also know that

  (iii) $\times$ is commutative;

  (iv) $[(x + 1, x)]$ is a *multiplicative identity* in Z;

    so

    $(Z, \times)$ is a commutative semi-group with identity.

$(Z, \times)$ is NOT a group, since not all integers have multiplicative inverses (see Exercise 3).

Addition and Multiplication

From our definitions of $+$ and $\times$ on Z it follows that

    $\times$ is distributive over $+$.

(See Exercise 4.)

Exercise 4

Show that

$$[(x, y)] \times ([(m, n)] + [(k, j)]) = [(x, y)] \times [(m, n)]$$
$$+ [(x, y)] \times [(k, j)].$$

∎

34.2.3 Relationship between the Integers and the Natural Numbers

We can map the set N of natural numbers to a subset of the integers by the one-one mapping

$$f : n \longmapsto [(1 + n, 1)] \qquad (n \in N).$$

We know that

$$[(1 + m, 1)] + [(1 + n, 1)] = [(2 + m + n, 2)]$$
$$= [(1 + m + n, 1)],$$

that is,

$$f(m) + f(n) = f(m + n),$$

and

$$[(1 + m, 1)] \times [(1 + n, 1)]$$
$$= [(1 + m + n + mn + 1, 1 + m + 1 + n)]$$
$$= [(1 + mn, 1)],$$

that is,

$$f(m) \times f(n) = f(m \times n).$$

So f is an *isomorphism* from the set of natural numbers to a subset of the set of integers for the operations $+$ and $\times$.

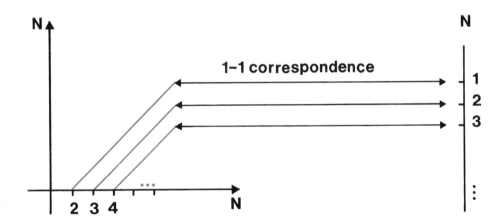

We use this isomorphism to simplify our notation for the integers. We can give the label n to the integer $[(1 + n, 1)]$, and operate with it as if it were a natural number.

Now not all integers are of the form $[(1 + n, 1)]$ for $n \in N$. One integer is of the form $[(n, n)]$, and we have seen that this integer is the additive identity, zero. The other integers are of the form $[(1, 1 + n)]$ for $n \in N$; the subset of Z comprising these integers is also isomorphic to N under addition for the mapping

$$f : n \longmapsto [(1, 1 + n)] \qquad (n \in N),$$

but it is NOT isomorphic to N under multiplication.

We indicate that members of this last subset behave under addition in the same way as the corresponding natural numbers, by giving the label $-n$ to the integer $[(1, 1 + n)]$. We give $[(n, n)]$ the label 0.

We call the set of integers of the form $[(1 + n, 1)]$ the set of *positive integers*, which we denote by Z^+, and the set of integers of the form $[(1, 1 + n)]$ the set of *negative integers*, which we denote by Z^-.

(continued on page 18)

Solution 34.2.2.4

Solution 34.2.2.4

$$[(x, y)] \times [(m + k, n + j)]$$

$$= [(xm + xk + yn + yj, xn + xj + ym + yk)]$$

$$= [(xm + yn, xn + ym) + (xk + yj, xj + yk)]$$

$$= [(x, y)] \times [(m, n)] + [(x, y)] \times [(k, j)].$$

Since $\times$ is commutative, it follows that

$$[(m + k, n + j)] \times [(x, y)] = [(m, n)] \times [(x, y)]$$
$$+ [(k, j)] \times [(x, y)].$$

So $\times$ is left- and right-distributive over $+$. ∎

(continued from page 17)

Exercise 1

Exercise 1
(2 minutes)

Show that, for all $a, b \in N$, the integer $[(a, b)]$ is equal to one of

$$[(1 + n, 1)], [(n, n)], [(1, 1 + n)],$$

where $n \in N$. ∎

An Order Relation on Z

We define the relation $<$ on Z by

Definition 1
* * *

$$[(m, n)] < [(m', n')]$$

if and only if

$$m + n' < m' + n.$$

(That is, we define $<$ on Z in terms of $<$ on N.)

We define the relation $\leqslant$ on Z by

Definition 2
* * *

$$[(m, n)] \leqslant [(m', n')]$$

if and only if

$$m + n' \leqslant m' + n.$$

(That is, we define $\leqslant$ on Z in terms of $\leqslant$ on N.)

Since $\leqslant$ is an order relation on N, it follows that $\leqslant$ is an order relation on Z.

Using the simplified notation for the integers, we can now write

$$\cdots \leqslant -3 \leqslant -2 \leqslant -1 \leqslant 0 \leqslant 1 \leqslant 2 \leqslant 3 \leqslant \cdots$$

Also we know that

$$-1 = -2 + 1$$
$$0 = -1 + 1$$

etc.

This means that we can represent the set of integers by equally spaced points on a number line:

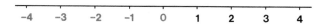

34.2.4 Divisibility

We have discussed the properties of addition and multiplication on the set of integers Z. We know that the equation

$$3x = 6$$

(in our simplified notation for integers) has a solution in Z, but the equation

$$6x = 3$$

has no solution in Z; that is, "division" is not a closed operation in Z. So although we cannot define "division" in Z to be an operation which "undoes" multiplication, we *can* define *divisibility*.

We say that an integer $a \neq 0$ is divisible by an integer b if there is an integer c such that

$$a = bc.$$

We shall call a a *multiple* of b (or c); b (or c) is said to *divide* a or to be a *divisor* or *factor* of a. We write

$b \mid a$ "b divides a",

$d \nmid a$ "d does not divide a".

For any $a \in Z$,

$$1, -1, a, -a$$

are all divisors of a.

If $a > 1$ and a has no other divisors, then a is a prime number. (1 is not regarded as a prime — we shall explain why later.) Prime numbers present all sorts of problems, such as the famous Goldbach conjecture: every even number greater than 2 is the sum of two primes. In a letter to Euler in 1742 Goldbach asked Euler if he could prove the statement or find a counter-example. The statement has not yet been proved or disproved, though it has been established that every even number greater than 4 is the sum of four primes. Another famous problem was to try to find a function of the natural number n — in particular, a polynomial function whose coefficients are natural numbers — whose images are all prime numbers. It was eventually shown that no such polynomial exists, but not before many sleepless nights had been spent.

Exercise 1

Show that, if a and b are non-zero integers such that

$$b|a \quad \text{and} \quad a|b,$$

then

$$a = \pm b.$$ ∎

Exercise 2

Show that, if $a, b, c, d, \alpha, \beta$ are integers such that

$$a = \alpha b + \beta c,$$

$$d|b \quad \text{and} \quad d|c,$$

then

$$d|a.$$ ∎

(continued on page 21)

Solution 34.2.3.1

Solution 34.2.3.1

For $a, b \in N$, we know that

$$a < b \quad \text{or} \quad a = b \quad \text{or} \quad b < a.$$

<u>$a < b$</u>

If $a < b$, $\exists_k \quad a + k = b \qquad (k \in N)$.

In this case,

$$[(a, b)] = [(1, 1 + n)], \qquad \text{where } n = k.$$

<u>$a = b$</u>

In this case,

$$[(a, a)] = [(n, n)], \qquad \text{where } a = n.$$

<u>$b < a$</u>

If $b < a$, $\exists_j \quad b + j = a \quad \cdot \quad (j \in N)$.

In this case,

$$[(a, b)] = [(1 + n, 1)], \qquad \text{where } n = j.$$

∎

Solution 1

Solution 1

$$b|a \Rightarrow \exists_c \qquad a = bc \qquad (c \in Z);$$
$$a|b \Rightarrow \exists_d \qquad b = ad \qquad (d \in Z).$$

So

$$a = bc = adc,$$

and by the cancellation rule $(a \neq 0)$, we have

$$1 = dc;$$

that is, either

$$d = c = 1$$

or

$$d = c = -1.$$

Hence

$$a = \pm b.$$

∎

Solution 2

Solution 2

$$d|b \Rightarrow \exists_m \qquad b = md \qquad (m \in Z);$$
$$d|c \Rightarrow \exists_n \qquad c = nd \qquad (n \in Z).$$

It follows that

$$a = \alpha b + \beta c$$
$$= \alpha m d + \beta n d$$
$$= (\alpha m + \beta n)d.$$

Now $\alpha m + \beta n \in Z$, and hence $d|a$.

∎

Highest Common Factors

Sometimes we need to know the largest number which divides two given integers. We define the highest common factor (h.c.f.) of the integers a and b to be the *positive* integer d such that

Definition 3
* * *

(i) $d|a$ and $d|b$;

and

(ii) whenever $c|a$ and $c|b$ ($c \in Z$), then $c|d$.

Condition (i) tells us that d is a *common factor* of a and b; condition (ii) tells us that d is the *largest* common factor.

We denote the highest common factor of a and b by (a, b):

Notation 2
* * *

$$d = (a, b).$$

If $(a, b) = 1$, then a and b have no common prime factor. In this case we say that a and b are co-prime or relatively prime.

Definition 4
* * *

If you found highest common factors at school, then you probably did so by expressing each of the integers a and b as a product of primes, and then finding the highest common factor by inspection. This method will obviously prove tedious if a and b are large, and in any case the method needs to be justified. Is it true that any integer can be expressed as a product of primes in only one way (disregarding order of primes and the sign of the integer)?

Before we answer this question, we shall discuss a method of finding the highest common factor of any two (positive) integers in a *finite* number of steps; it is called the Euclidean algorithm.

First we need the *division algorithm* which states that, if a and b are positive integers such that $a > b$, then there exist unique positive integers q and r such that

$$a = bq + r,$$

where

$$0 \leqslant r < b.$$

This is intuitively obvious. The set of integer multiples of b is a subset of Z. We can mark off the integer multiples of b on a "number line" on which the integers are marked, and, unless b divides a, the mark corresponding to a must lie between bq and $b(q + 1)$, say:

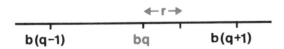

If we put $r = a - bq$, then $r < b$, so we have

$$a = bq + r, \quad \text{where} \quad 0 \leqslant r < b.$$

(If you would like to see a formal proof, you can find one in F. M. Hall, *Abstract Algebra*, Chapter 4 (see Bibliography).)

The Euclidean Algorithm

Let $a, b \in Z$, where $a > b > 0$.*

By the division algorithm, there exist $q_1, r_1 \in Z$ such that

$$a = bq_1 + r_1, \quad \text{where} \quad 0 \leqslant r_1 < b. \qquad \text{Equation (1)}$$

If $r_1 = 0$, then $b|a$, so $(a, b) = b$.

We shall use the results of Exercises 1 and 2 to show that, if $r_1 \neq 0$, then

$$(a, b) = (b, r_1).$$

From Equation (1) we can deduce that

> every integer which divides a and b divides r_1;
> hence every integer which divides a and b divides b and r_1

and so

> (a, b) divides b and r_1.

Now every integer which divides b and r_1 must divide (b, r_1), by definition of highest common factor. So we have

$$(a, b)|(b, r_1). \qquad \text{Statement (1)}$$

Similarly,

> every integer which divides b and r_1 divides a and b, so
> (b, r_1) divides a and b,

and hence

$$(b, r_1)|(a, b). \qquad \text{Statement (2)}$$

Using the result of Exercise 1, we deduce from Statements (1) and (2) that

$$(a, b) = (b, r_1).$$

This reduces the problem, but why stop here? Similarly, there exist integers q_2 and r_2 such that

$$b = r_1 q_2 + r_2, \quad \text{where} \quad 0 \leqslant r_2 < r_1,$$

and

$$(b, r_1) = (r_1, r_2).$$

We continue this reduction process until we obtain a zero remainder:

$$a = bq_1 + r_1, \quad \text{where} \quad 0 < r_1 < b$$
$$b = r_1 q_2 + r_2, \quad \text{where} \quad 0 < r_2 < r_1$$
$$r_1 = r_2 q_3 + r_3, \quad \text{where} \quad 0 < r_3 < r_2$$
$$\cdots$$
$$r_{n-2} = r_{n-1} q_n + r_n, \quad \text{where} \quad 0 < r_n < r_{n-1}$$
$$r_{n-1} = r_n q_{n+1} + 0.$$

The remainders decrease at each step, so we must obtain a zero remainder after a *finite* number of steps. We know that

$$(a, b) = (b, r_1) = (r_1, r_2) = \cdots = (r_{n-1}, r_n),$$

but, since the last remainder is zero,

$$r_n|r_{n-1}$$

and therefore

$$(a, b) = (r_{n-1}, r_n) = r_n.$$

---

* We take a and b to be positive as we have defined the h.c.f. to be positive.

That is,

(a, b) is the last non-zero remainder in the Euclidean algorithm.

Let us look at an example.

Example 1

Example 1

We shall find

$(5950, 1547)$.

Using the Euclidean algorithm, we obtain

$$5950 = 1547 \times 3 + 1309$$
$$1547 = 1309 \times 1 + 238$$
$$1309 = 238 \times 5 + 119$$
$$238 = 119 \times 2 + 0$$

The last non-zero remainder is 119; hence

$(5950, 1547) = 119$.　■

Exercise 3

Using the Euclidean algorithm, find:

 (i) $(6705, 345)$
(ii) $(429, 154)$.　■

Exercise 4

If you have time, draw a flow chart and write a program to find the highest common factor of two positive integers.

If you are short of time, use the program given in Solution 4 to find

 (i) $(5307, 9150)$
(ii) $(12000, 2904)$.　■　(*continued on page 26*)

Solution 3 **Solution 3**

(i) $6705 = 345 \times 19 + 150$

$\quad 345 = 150 \times 2 + 45$

$\quad 150 = 45 \times 3 + 15$

$\quad\ 45 = 15 \times 3 + 0.$

The last non-zero remainder is 15, hence

$$(6705, 345) = 15$$

(ii) $429 = 154 \times 2 + 121$

$\quad 154 = 121 \times 1 + 33$

$\quad 121 = 33 \times 3 + 22$

$\quad\ 33 = 22 \times 1 + 11$

$\quad\ 22 = 11 \times 2 + 0.$

The last non-zero remainder is 11, hence

$$(429, 154) = 11.$$

■

Solution 3

(i) $6705 = 345 \times 19 + 150$

$\quad 345 = 150 \times 2 + 45$

Solution 4

Solution 4

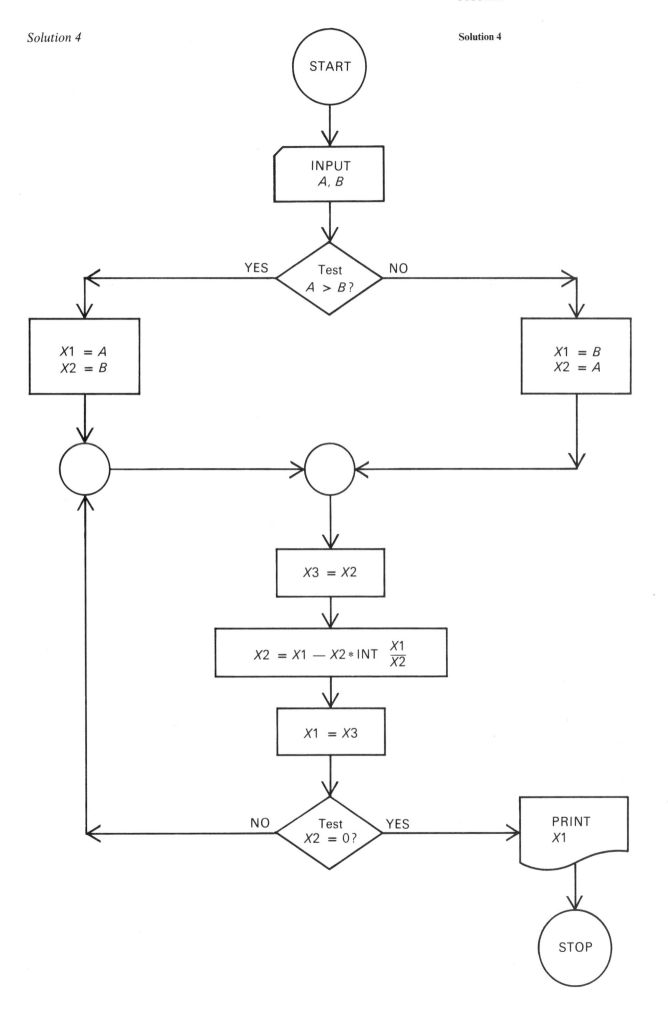

The following program is suitable:

```
GET-$EUCLID
LIST
EUCLID
9000   REM*****EUCLID*****MATHEMATICS PROGRAM*****
9001   REM*****VERSION 1*****7/31/69*****
9002   REM LARGEST COMMON FACTOR
9003   PRINT "WHAT ARE YOUR TWO INTEGERS";
9004   INPUT A, B
9005   LET X1=A
9006   IF A > B THEN 9009
9007   LET X1=B
9008   LET B=A
9009   LET X2=B
9010   DEF FNA(X)=X1/X2
9011   LET X3=X2
9012   LET X2=INT(X2*(FNA(1)-INT(FNA(1)))+.5)
9013   LET X1=X3
9014   IF X2 ≠ 0 THEN 9011
9015   PRINT "LARGEST COMMON FACTOR IS X1"
9016   STOP
9999   END
```

 (i) $(5307, 9150) = 183$
(ii) $(12000, 2904) = 24$ ■

(*continued from page 23*)

The Euclidean algorithm also gives us the following important theorem.

THEOREM

If a and b are positive integers and

$$d = (a, b),$$

then there exist integers α and β such that

$$d = \alpha a + \beta b.$$

PROOF

The result follows directly from the Euclidean algorithm. We express the successive remainders in terms of a and b:

$$r_1 = a - bq_1$$
$$r_2 = b - r_1 q_2 = b - (a - bq_1)q_2$$
$$= (-q_2)a + (1 + q_1 q_2)b$$
$$\cdots$$
$$r_n = \alpha a + \beta b, \quad \text{where } \alpha, \beta \in Z.$$

Example 2

In Example 1 we had

$$1309 = 5950 - 1547 \times 3$$
$$238 = 1547 - 1309$$
$$119 = 1309 - 238 \times 5$$

Example 2

Substituting for 1309 from the first equation in the second, we obtain

$$238 = 1547 - (5950 - 1547 \times 3)$$
$$= 4 \times 1547 - 5950.$$

Substituting for 1309 and 238 in the third equation, we have

$$119 = 5950 - 1547 \times 3 - (4 \times 1547 - 5950) \times 5.$$

Hence

$$119 = 6 \times 5950 + (-23) \times 1547.$$ ■

Note that the representation is *not unique*. For example,

$$(4, 2) = 2,$$

and we have

$$2 = -30 + 32 = 8 \times 4 + (-15) \times 2$$
$$2 = 4 - 2 = 1 \times 4 + (-1) \times 2$$
$$2 = 100 - 98 = 25 \times 4 + (-49) \times 2.$$

It is important to note that the theorem is an *existence theorem*. We are not really interested in *finding* the integers α and β, but we can use the fact *that they exist* to obtain useful results.

Theorem
* * *

THEOREM

If a, b, p are positive integers such that

$$(p, a) = 1 \quad \text{and} \quad p|ab,$$

then

$$p|b.$$

PROOF

$(p, a) = 1$, so by the previous theorem, there exist integers α and β such that

$$1 = \alpha p + \beta a.$$

Multiplying by b, we obtain

$$b = \alpha p b + \beta a b.$$

Now $p|ab$ and $p|p$, so p divides the right-hand side of the above equation; it must therefore divide the left-hand side, and hence

$$p|b.$$

COROLLARY

We can deduce that if p is a prime and $p|ab$, then either

$$p|b$$

or

$$p|a.$$

This follows immediately from the theorem, for since p is a prime,

$$p \nmid a \Rightarrow (p, a) = 1 \Rightarrow p|b,$$
$$p \nmid b \Rightarrow (p, b) = 1 \Rightarrow p|a.$$

Exercise 5

If a, b, c are positive integers such that

$$(a, b) = 1 \quad \text{and} \quad (a, c) = 1,$$

show that

$$(a, bc) = 1.$$ ■

Exercise 6

If $a, b \in Z^+$, $\alpha, \beta \in Z$ and

$$\alpha a + \beta b = 6,$$

what can be deduced about (a, b)? ■

34.2.5 The Fundamental Theorem of Arithmetic

We are now in a position to prove the following existence theorem.

FUNDAMENTAL THEOREM OF ARITHMETIC

Every integer $a \in Z$, except 0 and 1, has a representation of the form:

$$a = \pm p_1 p_2 \cdots p_n,$$

where the p_i's are prime numbers, and the representation is *unique* apart from the order of the factors. (The p_i's are not necessarily distinct.)

PROOF

The proof of the theorem falls into two parts: we first show that a representation exists, and then we show that the representation is unique.

(i) We use a proof by induction to show that a representation of the given form exists.

FIRST STEP

The theorem is true for $a = 2$.

SECOND STEP

We assume that a representation exists for all integers $a < k + 1$, for some $k \in Z$. Now *either* $k + 1$ is a prime and the statement is TRUE for $a = k + 1$, *or* $k + 1$ is composite, that is,

$$k + 1 = bc$$

where $b, c \in Z$, $b \neq 1$, $c \neq 1$.

It follows that $b < k + 1$ and $c < k + 1$. By hypothesis, we can represent b and c in the given form:

$$b = \pm p_\alpha \cdots p_\mu, \qquad c = \pm p_\beta \cdots p_\nu;$$

hence

$$k + 1 = \pm p_\alpha \cdots p_\mu p_\beta \cdots p_\nu.$$

We now have the representation of $k + 1$ in the required form.

(ii) Suppose there exist 2 representations of the given form for an integer a:

$$a = p_1 p_2 \cdots p_n = q_1 q_2 \cdots q_m,$$

where $1 \leqslant m$, $1 \leqslant n$, $m, n \in Z^+$.

We show that

$$m = n$$

and

$$\{p_1, p_2, \ldots, p_n\} = \{q_1, q_2, \ldots, q_m\}$$

We use a proof by induction on n.

FIRST STEP

When $n = 1$, then

$$p_1 = q_1 q_2 \cdots q_m.$$

But p_1 is a prime, and therefore

$$m = 1$$

and

$$p_1 = q_1.$$

So the conjucture is TRUE for $n = 1$.

SECOND STEP

We assume that the conjecture is TRUE when there are $(n - 1)$ factors on the left-hand side. We shall use the corollary on page 27:

If p is a prime and $p|ab$, then

$$\text{either} \quad p|a$$

$$\text{or} \quad p|b.$$

We have

$$p_1 p_2 \cdots p_n = q_1 q_2 \cdots q_m.$$

Now p_1 divides the left-hand side, and so

$$p_1 | q_1 q_2 \cdots q_m.$$

If $p_1 \neq q_1$, then $(p_1, q_1) = 1$, since p_1 and q_1 are both primes. Now

$$(p_1, q_1) = 1 \Rightarrow p_1 | q_2 q_3 \cdots q_m.$$

If $p_1 \neq q_2$, then $(p_1, q_2) = 1$, and

$$(p_1, q_2) = 1 \Rightarrow p_1 | q_3 \cdots q_m$$

etc.

We see that

$$p_1 | q_j \text{ for some } j \in Z, \qquad 1 \leqslant j \leqslant m$$

$$\Rightarrow p_1 = q_j, \text{ since } q_j \text{ is a prime.}$$

By the cancellation rule, we have

$$p_2 p_3 \cdots p_n = q_1 q_2 \cdots q_{j-1} q_{j+1} \cdots q_m.$$

The left-hand side now has $(n - 1)$ factors, and so, by hypothesis,

$$n - 1 = m - 1$$

and

$$\{p_2, p_3, \ldots, p_n\} = \{q_1, q_2, \ldots, q_{j-1}, q_{j+1}, \ldots, q_m\}$$

Hence

$$m = n$$

and

$$\{p_1, p_2, \ldots, p_n\} = \{q_1, q_2, \ldots, q_m\}$$

(*continued on page 30*)

Solution 34.2.4.5

Solution 34.2.4.5

$(a, b) = 1 \Rightarrow$ there exist $\alpha, \beta \in Z$ such that

$$\alpha a + \beta b = 1 \, ;$$

$(a, c) = 1 \Rightarrow$ there exist $\gamma, \delta \in Z$ such that

$$\gamma a + \delta c = 1.$$

Multiplying these two equations together gives

$$(\alpha a + \beta b)(\gamma a + \delta c) = 1$$

i.e.

$$a(\alpha \gamma a + \beta b \gamma + \alpha \delta c) + bc(\beta \delta) = 1.$$

Hence any integer which divides a and bc divides the left-hand side and hence divides 1. It follows that

$$(a, bc) = 1. \qquad \blacksquare$$

Solution 34.2.4.6

Solution 34.2.4.6

$$(a, b) \text{ divides } 6 \, ;$$

that is,

$$(a, b) = 1 \quad \text{or} \quad 2 \quad \text{or} \quad 3 \quad \text{or} \quad 6.$$

It does NOT follow that $(a, b) = 6$. For example, if $a = 4$, $b = 2$, then

$$1 \times a + 1 \times b = 6$$

but

$$(a, b) \neq 6. \qquad \blacksquare$$

(*continued from page 29*)

We have shown that every integer has a unique representation (order apart) as a product of primes.

(If we regarded 1 as a prime, we would not have a *unique* representation as we could include in the representation any numbers of 1's.)

This theorem justifies the method of finding the highest common factor of two integers by the method described on page 21.

34.3   THE RATIONAL NUMBERS

34.3.0   Introduction

We defined the integers in order to provide a solution to the equation

$$m + x = n$$

for all integers m and n, taking care that the set of integers contained a subset isomorphic to our original set of natural numbers for the operation of addition.

We find a similar need for the "enrichment" of the system of integers when we consider the equation

$$mx = n.$$

The equation $3x = 6$ has an integer as its solution, but the equation $6x = 3$ does not have a solution in Z. If m and n are integers, then there is not necessarily an integer x which satisfies the equation $mx = n$. Again we overcome this problem by "extending" the number system: we introduce a new type of number and new operations which have the required properties. To do this, we use an equivalence relation on the set of ordered pairs of integers; we call the new numbers *rational numbers* (rationals), and denote the set of rationals by Q. Again we take care that the set of rationals contains a subset isomorphic to the set of integers, under defined operations. As this procedure is similar to that used in the construction of the integers, we shall not give all the details, but list the main points.

Notice that we "enrich" each number system so that the new system has more "powerful" properties than its predecessor but contains a subsystem isomorphic to the previous system, so that nothing is lost.

34.3.1   Construction of the Rationals

If m is any integer, and n is any integer except 0, we call (m, n) an *integer pair*.

We define a relationship ρ_2 on the set of integer pairs by

$$(m, n)\rho_2(m', n')$$

if and only if

$$mn' = m'n.$$

(Note that this definition is given in terms of multiplication of integers.)

One immediate conclusion is that

$$(mx, nx)\rho_2(m, n) \quad \text{for all } x \neq 0.$$

It is easy to show that ρ_2 is an *equivalence relation*. We define the corresponding equivalence classes to be rational numbers. We shall denote the class to which (m, n) belongs by $[(m, n)]$.

We denote the set of rationals by Q.

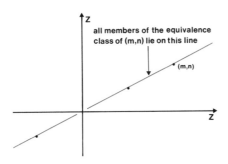

34.3.2 Arithmetical Operations on Q

The rational number system has the following properties:

(i) The rationals $[(m, n)]$ and $[(m', n')]$ will be the same if

$$mn' = m'n;$$

in this case we write

$$[(m, n)] = [(m', n')].$$

(ii) The operation of addition on the set of integer pairs is defined by

$$(m_1, n_1) + (m_2, n_2) = (m_1 n_2 + m_2 n_1, n_1 n_2).$$

The operation of addition of integer pairs is compatible with the relation ρ_2.

Addition of rationals is defined by

$$[(m_1, n_1)] + [(m_2, n_2)] = [(m_1 n_2 + m_2 n_1, n_1 n_2)].$$

(iii) $+$ is a closed binary operation on Q;
$+$ is commutative;
$+$ is associative.
These properties follow immediately from the properties of addition on Z.

(iv)
$$[(m, n)] + [(0, 1)] = [(m, n)],$$
$$[(0, 1)] + [(m, n)] = [(m, n)].$$

That is, $[(0, 1)]$ is an *identity element* for addition. It is unique. The rational $[(0, 1)]$ is called *zero*.

(v)
$$[(m, n)] + [(-m, n)] = [(0, 1)];$$

that is, $[(-m, n)]$ is an *additive inverse* of $[(m, n)]$. It is unique.

(vi) The equation

$$[(m', n')] + [(x, y)] = [(m, n)]$$

has the unique solution

$$[(x, y)] = [(mn' - m'n, n'n)].$$

(Note that mn' and $m'n$ are integers, and subtraction of integers has already been defined; also that, if $n \neq 0$ and $n' \neq 0$, then $n'n \neq 0$, so $(mn' - m'n, n'n)$ *is* an integer pair.)

(vii) If

$$[(m, n)] + [(x, y)] = [(m', n')] + [(x, y)],$$

then

$$[(m, n)] = [(m', n')];$$

this is a *cancellation law* for addition.

(viii) The operation of *subtraction* on the set of rationals is defined by

$$[(m, n)] - [(m', n')] = [(x, y)]$$

if and only if

$$[(m, n)] = [(x, y)] + [(m', n')].$$

(ix) The operation of multiplication on the set of integer pairs is defined by

$$(m_1, n_1) \times (m_2, n_2) = (m_1 m_2, n_1 n_2).$$

The operation of multiplication of integer pairs is compatible with the relation ρ_2.

Multiplication of rationals is defined by

$$[(m_1, n_1)] \times [(m_2, n_2)] = [(m_1 m_2, n_1 n_2)].$$

(x) $\times$ is a closed binary operation on Q;
  $\times$ is commutative;
  $\times$ is associative.

These properties follow immediately from the properties of multiplication on Z.

(xi) $[(m, n)] \times [(1, 1)] = [(m, n)]$

    $[(1, 1)] \times [(m, n)] = [(m, n)]$

That is, $[(1, 1)]$ is an *identity element* for multiplication. It is unique. The rational $[(1, 1)]$ is called *unity*.

(xii) $[(m, n)] \times [(n, m)] = [(1, 1)],$

where

    $[(m, n)] \neq [(0, 1)];$

that is, $[(n, m)]$ is the *multiplicative inverse* of $[(m, n)]$, where

    $[(m, n)] \neq [(0, 1)].$

(xiii) The equation

    $[(m', n')] \times [(x, y)] = [(m, n)]$

has the unique solution

    $[(x, y)] = [(mn', m'n)].$

(xiv) If

    $[(m, n)] \times [(x, y)] = [(m', n')] \times [(x, y)],$

where

    $[(x, y)] \neq [(0, 1)],$

then

    $[(m, n)] = [(m', n')];$

this is a *cancellation law* for multiplication.

(xv) The operation of *division* on the set of rationals is defined by

    $[(m, n)] \div [(m', n')] = [(x, y)]$

if and only if

    $[(m, n)] = [(x, y)] \times [(m', n')],$

where $[(m', n')] \neq [(0, 1)]$.

(xvi) $[(x, y)] \times ([(m, n)] + [(m', n')])$

    $= [(x, y)] \times [(m, n)] +$

    $[(x, y)] \times [(m', n')]$

and

    $([(m, n)] + [(m', n')]) \times [(x, y)]$

    $= [(m, n)] \times [(x, y)] +$

    $[(m', n')] \times [(x, y)];$

i.e. multiplication is distributive over addition.

Summary

$(Q, +)$ is an Abelian group.
(See properties (iii), (iv) and (v).)
$(Q_1, \times)$ is an Abelian group, where Q_1 is the set of non-zero rationals.
(See properties (x), (xi) and (xii).)
$-$ and $\div$ are operations which "undo" $+$ and $\times$ respectively.
$\times$ is distributive over $+$.

34.3.3 Relationship between the Integers and the Rationals

We can map the set Z of integers to a subset of the rationals by the one-one mapping

$$f : n \longmapsto [(n, 1)] \qquad (n \in Z).$$

We know that

$$[(n, 1)] + [(m, 1)] = [(m + n, 1)],$$

that is,

$$f(n) + f(m) = f(m + n),$$

and

$$[(n, 1)] \times [(m, 1)] = [(mn, 1)],$$

that is,

$$f(n) \times f(m) = f(m \times n).$$

So f is an isomorphism from the set of integers to a subset of the set of rationals, for addition and multiplication.

We use this isomorphism to simplify our notation for the rationals. We can give the label n to the rational $[(n, 1)]$, and operate with it as if it were an integer. For this reason, the rationals $\{[(n, 1)]\}$ are sometimes called *pseudo-integers*.

When we had completed our construction of the integers, we devised a label for each integer which is more convenient to use than the cumbersome equivalence-class notation. We now do the same for rationals, and give the label $\dfrac{m}{n}$ to the rational $[(m, n)]$, where $n \neq 0$. We see that

$$\frac{\lambda m}{\lambda n} = [(\lambda m, \lambda n)] = [(m, n)] = \frac{m}{n},$$

where λ is a non-zero integer.

If m and n have highest common factor d, then

$$\frac{m}{n} = \frac{m'd}{n'd} = \frac{m'}{n'}$$

where $m', n' \in Z$ and m' and n' are co-prime. In this form, the rational is said to be in its *lowest terms*.

We can now carry out arguments on the rationals in the notation already familiar to you.

Example 1

Show that there is no rational whose square is 2. ∎

Example 1

Solution of Example 1

Suppose that there is such a rational, and that when expressed in its lowest terms it is $\dfrac{m}{n}$.

Then

$$\frac{m^2}{n^2} = 2$$

i.e.

$$m^2 = 2n^2, \qquad \text{so } m \text{ is even (the square of an odd integer is odd).}$$

Suppose

$$m = 2x, \qquad \text{where } x \in Z.$$

We have

$$4x^2 = 2n^2, \qquad \text{so } n \text{ is also even.}$$

But this is a contradiction, for, by hypothesis, m and n are co-prime, and do not have 2 as a common factor.

This contradiction arises from the supposition that a rational whose square is 2 exists; therefore there is *no* rational whose square is equal to 2. ∎

Note that, since $\dfrac{(-1)m}{(-1)n} = \dfrac{m}{n}$, we can write $\dfrac{m}{-n}$ as $\dfrac{-m}{n}$. That is, we can express any rational in the form $\dfrac{m}{n}$, where $n \in Z^{+}$.

We define the relation $<$ on Q by

$$\frac{m}{n} < \frac{m'}{n'},$$

where $n, n' \in Z^{+}$, if and only if

$$mn' < m'n.$$

We define the relation $\leqslant$ on Q by

$$\frac{m}{n} \leqslant \frac{m'}{n'},$$

where $n, n' \in Z^{+}$, if and only if

$$mn' \leqslant m'n.$$

That is, we define $<$ and $\leqslant$ on Q in terms of the relations $<$ and $\leqslant$ on Z. It follows that $\leqslant$ is an order relation on Q. This relation enables us to represent the rationals by points on a number line:

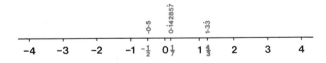

$\dfrac{m}{n} \; (n \in Z^{+})$ occurs to the left of $\dfrac{m'}{n'} \; (n' \in Z^{+})$ if $\dfrac{m}{n} < \dfrac{m'}{n'}$.

34.3.4 Sets of Rationals

When we discussed properties of the natural numbers, we stated that every set of natural numbers has a least member. Although exactly the same statement does not hold for the integers, several slightly modified statements do hold. For example, every set of positive integers has a least member; every set of negative integers has a greatest member; if every member of a set A of integers is greater than some integer l, then A has a least member; if every member of a set A of integers is less than some integer g then A has a greatest member. Subsets of the rationals do not necessarily have these properties. For example, the set

$$A = \left\{ \frac{1}{2^n} : n = 1, 2, \ldots \right\}$$

has no least member.

However, it is clear that $0 \leqslant a$ for all $a \in A$.

In the general case, if A is a set of rationals, and if there is a rational l such that $l \leqslant a$ for every $a \in A$, then l is called a *lower bound* for A. Notice that l need not belong to A.

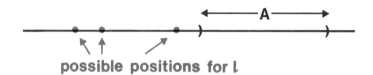

possible positions for l

As A has a lower bound, we say it is *bounded below*. For example, the set $A = \left\{ \frac{2^n}{3} : n = 1, 2, \ldots \right\}$ is bounded below, but it is not bounded above.

Exercise 1

Find upper and lower bounds for each of the following sets:

(i) $\left\{ 1 - \frac{1}{2^n} : n = 1, 2, \ldots \right\}$

(ii) $\left\{ \frac{1}{(-2)^n} : n = 1, 2, \ldots \right\}$

(iii) $\left\{ \frac{1}{10}, \frac{11}{100}, \frac{111}{1000}, \frac{1111}{10\,000}, \ldots \right\}$ ■

The last exercise contains the essence of what is to follow. If l is a lower bound of a subset A of Q, then so also is $l - x$ for any positive rational x.

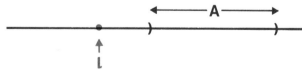

In other words, we can always find a *lower* lower bound. But can we find a *greater* lower bound? In particular, is there a *greatest* lower bound? The last exercise suggests that the existence of a (rational) lower bound of a set of rationals implies the existence of a (rational) greatest lower bound. But consider the set of all values given by the sequence $\{u_n\}$ where

$$u_1 = 2$$

$$u_{n+1} = \frac{u_n}{2} + \frac{1}{u_n} \qquad (n > 1).$$

Now

$$u_1^2 - 2 = 2,$$

so $2 < u_1^2$. Also

$$u_{n+1}^2 - 2 = \left(\frac{u_n}{2} + \frac{1}{u_n}\right)^2 - 2$$

$$= \left(\frac{u_n}{2} - \frac{1}{u_n}\right)^2$$

$$= \left(\frac{u_n^2 - 2}{2u_n}\right)^2.$$

Hence $2 < u_n^2$ for all n. (A square is non-negative, and since $u_n \in Q, u_n^2 \neq 2$, by Example 34.3.3.1, so $0 < u_{n+1}^2 - 2$.) Further,

$$u_n - u_{n+1} = u_n - \left(\frac{u_n}{2} + \frac{1}{u_n}\right)$$

$$= \frac{u_n}{2} - \frac{1}{u_n}$$

$$= \frac{u_n^2 - 2}{2u_n};$$

it follows that $0 < u_n - u_{n+1}$ for all n, since $2 < u_n^2$ and u_n^2 is positive for all n.

So the sequence $u_1, u_2, u_3, \ldots$ decreases perpetually, but $\{u_i\}$ has a lower bound, for example, 1, since $1^2 < 2$ and $2 < u_n^2$ for all n.

Suppose there is a greatest lower bound l. Then $l \leqslant u_n$ for all n, and $u_n \leqslant l + \varepsilon$ (where ε is positive) for all n beyond a certain point (for otherwise $l + \varepsilon$ would also be a lower bound, which is impossible as l is the *greatest* lower bound).

Hence for all n beyond a certain point, u_n lies within the interval $[l, l + \varepsilon]$: and this is true however small we take ε. But this is exactly how we define a limit. Therefore u_n approaches l as n increases. Now $u_{n+1} = \frac{u_n}{2} + \frac{1}{u_n}$ and u_n approaches l, u_{n+1} approaches l. Hence

$$l = \frac{l}{2} + \frac{1}{l}$$

$\therefore$

$$\frac{l}{2} = \frac{1}{l}$$

i.e.

$$l^2 = 2.$$

But there is no such rational l, since in Example 34.3.3.1, we showed that there is no rational whose square equals 2.

All this argument and final contradiction springs from the supposition that there is a rational which is the greatest lower bound to the set of rationals $\{u_i\}$ defined above. Therefore there is no such rational greatest lower bound.

Solution 1

   (i) Any value $\leqslant \frac{1}{2}$ is a lower bound.
       Any value a where $1 \leqslant a$ is an upper bound.
  (ii) Any value $\leqslant -\frac{1}{2}$ is a lower bound.
       Any value a where $\frac{1}{4} \leqslant a$ is an upper bound.
 (iii) Any value $\leqslant \frac{1}{10}$ is a lower bound.
       Any value a where $\frac{1}{9} \leqslant a$ is an upper bound. ■

34.4 REAL NUMBERS

34.4.0 Introduction

We constructed the integers from the natural numbers because we required a number system in which an equation of the form

$$m + x = n$$

always had a solution. We then constructed the rationals from the integers because we required a number system in which an equation of the form

$$m \times x = n$$

always had a solution.

Even with the rationals, we have come across two "deficiencies":

(i) the equation $x^2 = 2$ has no rational solution;
(ii) not all sets of rationals which are bounded below have rational greatest lower bounds.

Our discussion at the end of section 34.3.4 suggests that these deficiencies are connected. We begin by considering (i).

Given any line, we would like to associate points on it with numbers, namely the distances of those points from some origin O. If we are to finish with no "gaps" in our system, there must be a number corresponding to every point.

For example, given the point P on the line, we would like to associate a number, x say, with P (x being the distance OP). If P is such that $OP^2 = 2$, then there is no such x, for the only x's at our disposal at present are the rationals.

If we cannot take a rational, we might think of taking the greatest rational which has its corresponding point to the left of P. But once again we are thwarted, for there is no such greatest rational. The only "building bricks" at our disposal are the rationals, so we have to find some way of "tying down" the position of P in terms of the rationals.

Now there is one distinctive relationship between P and the rationals: it divides them into two classes, a Left-hand class and a Right-hand class. Moreover, different points P and P' partition the rationals into different classes. This suggests that we can achieve our object by defining our new numbers in terms of partitioned classes of rationals.

Do not despair if you find the construction of the real numbers hard to understand. The essential point to grasp is that the real number system *can* be constructed from the rational number system by a procedure which is logically sound.

34.4.1   Construction of the Real Numbers

We take all the rationals and divide them into two classes, $\mathscr{L}$ (for left-hand) and $\mathscr{R}$ (for right-hand), as follows:

  I each rational belongs either to $\mathscr{L}$ or to $\mathscr{R}$;
  II each member of $\mathscr{L}$ is less than each member of $\mathscr{R}$;
 III neither $\mathscr{L}$ nor $\mathscr{R}$ is empty.

We can make some immediate observations:

(a) No rational can belong to both $\mathscr{L}$ and $\mathscr{R}$; for otherwise II would be violated.
(b) The set $\mathscr{L}$ is bounded above; for any member of $\mathscr{R}$ is an upper bound. Similarly, $\mathscr{R}$ is bounded below.
(c) $\mathscr{L}$ cannot contain a greatest rational l if $\mathscr{R}$ contains a least rational r.

For if this occurred, $\dfrac{l+r}{2}$ would be a rational belonging to neither $\mathscr{L}$ nor $\mathscr{R}$, which violates I.

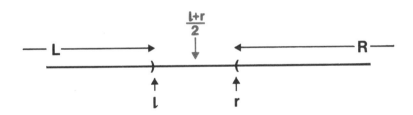

(d) $\mathscr{L}$ may contain a greatest rational. For example, suppose $a \in \mathscr{L}$ if $a \leqslant 0$, $b \in \mathscr{R}$ if $0 < b$, then $\mathscr{L}$ contains a greatest rational, namely 0.
(e) Similarly, $\mathscr{R}$ may contain a least rational.
(f) If $\mathscr{L}$ has a greatest rational l, then $a \leqslant l$ for all $a \in \mathscr{L}$;
   ∴ l is an upper bound for $\mathscr{L}$. Also $l - \delta < l \in \mathscr{L}$, where δ is positive.
   ∴ $l - \delta$ is not an upper bound for any δ;
   ∴ l is the *least* (rational) upper bound.
(g) Similarly, if $\mathscr{R}$ has a least rational r, then r is the *greatest* (rational) lower bound.
(h) $\mathscr{L}$ and $\mathscr{R}$ may both be without boundary member (i.e. $\mathscr{L}$ has no greatest member and $\mathscr{R}$ has no least member). For example, suppose $b \in \mathscr{R}$ if $0 < b$ and $2 < b^2$, and every other rational $\in \mathscr{L}$.

If $\mathscr{R}$ has a least member, it must be the greatest (rational) lower bound of the set, by (g). But the positive rationals whose squares are greater than 2 have no greatest (rational) lower bound.

     ∴ $\mathscr{R}$ has no least member.

A similar argument shows that $\mathscr{L}$ has no greatest member in this case.

(i) We can find $a \in \mathscr{L}$, $b \in \mathscr{R}$, such that $b - a = c$, where c is any positive rational. For if we start with any $a_1 \in \mathscr{L}$, then $b_1 = a_1 + c$ is a rational. If $b_1 \in \mathscr{R}$, we have succeeded. If not, take $a_2 = b_1 \in \mathscr{L}$ and try $b_2 = a_2 + c$. In time we must reach a first rational b_n which belongs to $\mathscr{R}$, as $\mathscr{L}$ is bounded above. In this case $a_n \in \mathscr{L}$, $b_n \in \mathscr{R}$ and $b_n - a_n = c$.

With one qualification, we now define any such class of rationals $\mathscr{L}$ to be a real number. The qualification is that if $\mathscr{L}$ has a greatest member l, and $\mathscr{L}'$ is the class obtained from $\mathscr{L}$ by the omission of the single rational l, then we accept the real numbers $\mathscr{L}$ and $\mathscr{L}'$ as being equal.

Definition 1
* * *

The qualification may look untidy; but there is an intrinsic difficulty here, and some such device is unavoidable. It amounts to the fact that on those occasions when $\mathscr{L}$ or $\mathscr{R}$ has a boundary member, there are two ways of expressing the same real number. But this is quite familiar to you already; you are used to the fact that $\frac{1}{2}$ in decimals can be expressed either as

$$0.5 \quad \text{or as} \quad 0.49999\ldots$$

It creates no difficulties in practice; we merely take the form which is the more convenient in a particular situation. Indeed, the example shows rather more than this. In the form "0.5", we are thinking of the rational $\frac{1}{2}$ as belonging to the set $\mathscr{L}$. In the form "0.49999...", we are thinking of the rational $\frac{1}{2}$ as not belonging to the set $\mathscr{L}'$. To say that $\mathscr{L}$ and $\mathscr{L}'$ are expressions of the same real number is equivalent to saying that 0.5 and 0.49999... are equal.

The Pseudo-Rationals

Just as rationals include the pseudo-integers, so the reals include the pseudo-rationals. It does not take much intuition to see that the real number $\mathscr{L}$, consisting of rationals satisfying $a \leqslant l$, where l is a rational, is equivalent in all material respects to the rational l itself. More will be said about this when we come to the arithmetical operations. The pseudo-rationals arise precisely when $\mathscr{L}$ or $\mathscr{R}$ has a boundary member; the real number $\mathscr{L}$ is then equivalent to this rational (in the same sort of way that the rational $\frac{m}{1}$ is equivalent to the integer m). If neither $\mathscr{L}$ nor $\mathscr{R}$ has a boundary member, the real number $\mathscr{L}$ is not a pseudo-rational, and there is no ambiguity in the expression for the number.

If a rational is itself a pseudo-integer, the pseudo-rational equivalent to it is a pseudo-pseudo-integer! (though we do not persevere with the double pseudo). Two special pseudo-integers are

zero, given by $\mathscr{L}$ whose members satisfy $a \leqslant 0$

and

unity given by $\mathscr{L}$ whose members satisfy $a \leqslant 1$.

Given any two reals $\mathscr{L}_1$ and $\mathscr{L}_2$, we say that $\mathscr{L}_1 < \mathscr{L}_2$ if $\mathscr{R}_1$ contains any rational (other than a boundary member) which belongs to $\mathscr{L}_2$. We say that $\mathscr{L}_1 \leqslant \mathscr{L}_2$ if $\mathscr{L}_1$ is a subset of $\mathscr{L}_2$.

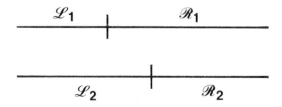

It can be shown that $\leqslant$ is an order relation on the set of real numbers R. This follows from the properties of the relation $\leqslant$ on Q.

34.4.2 Arithmetical Operations on R

Addition

Given any two reals $\mathscr{L}_1$ and $\mathscr{L}_2$, we may form the class $\mathscr{L}$ of all rationals obtainable by adding each rational in $\mathscr{L}_1$ to each rational in $\mathscr{L}_2$. Any rational not so obtainable we put into a class $\mathscr{R}$. As we do not wish to make heavy weather of the question, we shall rely on intuition to reveal that $\mathscr{L}$ and $\mathscr{R}$ satisfy the conditions I, II and III. We call $\mathscr{L}$ the sum of the real numbers $\mathscr{L}_1$ and $\mathscr{L}_2$, and we write

Main Text
* *

Definition 1
* * *

$$\mathscr{L}_1 + \mathscr{L}_2 = \mathscr{L}.$$

If $\mathscr{L}_1$ consists of rationals $\leqslant l_1$, and $\mathscr{L}_2$ consists of rationals $\leqslant l_2$, the sum of the pseudo-rationals $\mathscr{L}_1$ and $\mathscr{L}_2$ is the pseudo-rational $\mathscr{L}$ consisting of rationals $\leqslant l_1 + l_2$.

Addition of reals is commutative and associative. Zero is the *identity element* for addition.

These properties follow from the properties of rational numbers.

Exercise 1

Exercise 1
(5 minutes)

If $\mathscr{L}_1$ is any positive real, and $\mathscr{L}_2$ is the real consisting of all rationals $-a$, where $a \in \mathscr{R}_1$, demonstrate that $\mathscr{L}_1 + \mathscr{L}_2 = 0$. ∎

Subtraction

In Exercise 1, $\mathscr{L}_2$ is the *additive inverse* of $\mathscr{L}_1$, and it would be consistent to write

$$\mathscr{L}_2 = -\mathscr{L}_1.$$

If we are now faced with the equation

$$\mathscr{L}_1 + X = \mathscr{L}_2,$$

we take $X = \mathscr{L}_2 + (-\mathscr{L}_1)$, so that

$$\mathscr{L}_1 + X = \mathscr{L}_1 + (-\mathscr{L}_1) + \mathscr{L}_2$$
$$= 0 + \mathscr{L}_2$$
$$= \mathscr{L}_2.$$

(using the commutative and associate properties of $+$, and the identity element)

Moreover if $X \neq X'$

$$\mathscr{L}_1 + X' \neq \mathscr{L}_1 + X = \mathscr{L}_2$$

so the solution is unique.

Multiplication

If $\mathscr{L}_1$ and $\mathscr{L}_2$ are positive reals, and $a_1 \in \mathscr{R}_1$, $a_2 \in \mathscr{R}_2$, we form the class $\mathscr{R}$ of all products $a_1 a_2$. It can now be seen that $\mathscr{R}$ together with its complement $\mathscr{L}$ satisfy conditions I, II and III, so $\mathscr{L}$ is a real number which is defined to be the product of $\mathscr{L}_1$ and $\mathscr{L}_2$; we write

Definition 2
* * *

$$\mathscr{L}_1 \times \mathscr{L}_2 = \mathscr{L} \quad \text{or} \quad \mathscr{L}_1 \mathscr{L}_2 = \mathscr{L}.$$

In order to maintain the isomorphism of the pseudo-rationals to the rationals, for multiplication, we make the following further definitions.

If $\mathscr{L}_2$ is negative, we define $\mathscr{L}_1 \mathscr{L}_2$ to be the real $-\mathscr{L}_1(-\mathscr{L}_2)$. Similarly, if $\mathscr{L}_1$ and $\mathscr{L}_2$ are both negative, we define their product to be $(-\mathscr{L}_1)(-\mathscr{L}_2)$.

If $\mathscr{L}_1$ contains a greatest rational l_1, and $\mathscr{L}_2$ contains a greatest rational l_2, it is easy to see that the product $\mathscr{L}_1 \mathscr{L}_2$ is the pseudo-rational corresponding to $l_1 l_2$.

(*continued on page 42*)

Solution 1

If $x \in \mathscr{L}_1$, $y \in \mathscr{L}_2$, then $y = -a$, where $a \in \mathscr{R}_1$.

$$\therefore \quad x + y = x - a < 0 \qquad \text{for all } x \text{ and } a,$$

since every member of $\mathscr{L}_1$ is less than every member of $\mathscr{R}_1$. Therefore all members of $\mathscr{L}_1 + \mathscr{L}_2$ are negative. Conversely, if $-z$ is any negative rational, we can find $x \in \mathscr{L}_1$ and $a \in \mathscr{R}_1$ such that

$$a - x = z$$

Therefore we can find $x \in \mathscr{L}_1$ and $y = -a \in \mathscr{L}_2$ such that

$$x + y = x - a = -z.$$

Therefore all negative rationals, and only negative rationals, can be obtained as a sum $x + y$, where $x \in \mathscr{L}_1$, $y \in \mathscr{L}_2$. Therefore the sum class $\mathscr{L}$ consists of all negative rationals, and so the real number $\mathscr{L}$ is the pseudo-integer 0. ∎

(continued from page 41)

We can now establish the usual arithmetical laws, though to do so once again would be rather a chore.

Multiplication of reals is commutative and associative.

> 1 is the *identity element* for multiplication.
> $\times$ is distributive over $+$.

Division

Given any positive real $\mathscr{L}$, we define its reciprocal to be $\mathscr{L}'$, where $\mathscr{L}'$ contains the multiplicative inverses of the rationals in $\mathscr{R}$. It follows that

Definition 3
* * *

$$\mathscr{L}\mathscr{L}' = 1$$

i.e. $\mathscr{L}'$ is the *multiplicative inverse* of $\mathscr{L}$.

We can write the reciprocal of $\mathscr{L}$ as $\dfrac{1}{\mathscr{L}}$.

We define the reciprocal of $-\mathscr{L}$ to be $-\left(\dfrac{1}{\mathscr{L}}\right)$.

Reciprocals enable us to divide. For, given the equation

$$\mathscr{L}_1 X = \mathscr{L}_2, \; \mathscr{L}_1 \neq 0,$$

there is the unique solution

$$X = \mathscr{L}_2 \times \frac{1}{\mathscr{L}_1}.$$

Summary

Summary
* * *

We have defined $+$ and $\times$ on R such that

> $(R, +)$ is an Abelian group,
> $(R^+ \cup R^-, \times)$ is an Abelian group,
> $\times$ is distributive over $+$.

34.4.3   Filling the "Gaps"

When dealing with rationals, we found there were "deficiencies". For example, no rational has its square equal to 2; a set of rationals bounded above does not necessarily possess a least (rational) upper bound. We now ask: have we overcome these problems by defining the real numbers? The answer is Yes.

We shall now give an outline of a proof of a form of this, namely that a set S of pseudo-rationals which is bounded above possesses a least (real) upper bound. The proof involves side-stepping from pseudo-rationals to rationals, so it looks simpler in tabular form:

Pseudo-rationals	Rationals
$A \in$ the given set S. $\longrightarrow$	Consider the rational a corresponding to A, and let the set of all such a be s.
We know that S is bounded above, $\longrightarrow$	so s is bounded above.
	(i) If s possesses a greatest member t,
then S possesses a greatest member T (corresponding to t), and T is the least upper bound of S.	
	(ii) If s has no greatest member augment s by including all rationals less than any element of s. Call this augmented set s'. Then every rational either belongs to s' or does not, so s' and its complement satisfy I, II and III: this therefore defines a real, which is the least real upper bound of S.

It follows from this result that there is a real number whose square equals 2.

Knowing that such a class exists, we denote it by $\sqrt{2}$. Similarly for other roots.

It can also be shown that, if S_1 is a set of real numbers bounded above, then S_1 possesses a least real upper bound. This is called Dedekind's Theorem. A proof is given in G. H. Hardy, *Pure Mathematics* (Cambridge University Press, 1967), Chapter 1.

34.4.4   Representation of Real Numbers

The reals have been defined; but it is difficult to see at first glance how to obtain a single value from a set of rationals. And anyway, how do we represent the value even when we can grasp it? All we have to use basically are the natural numbers $1, 2, 3, \ldots$ (or the equivalent non-zero integers) and zero. Therefore we must find a way of using these natural numbers — or combinations of them — to represent and convey the numerical value of any real x. For convenience, we take x to be positive; for negative x all we need do is to express $-x$ and then affix a minus sign in front of the expression.

If x is a pseudo-integer (or zero), we can express its value immediately in terms of a single element from the set

$$\{0, 1, 2, 3, 4, 5, 6, 7, 8, 9, 10, 11, \ldots\}.$$

If not, we can take out the integer part of it, leaving a remainder which lies between 0 and 1. i.e. $x = a_0 + x_1$ where a_0 is a non-negative integer and $0 < x_1 < 1$.

We cannot take out any integer part of x_1. But we notice that $1 < \dfrac{1}{x_1}$; and we would have some idea of x_1 if we knew the integer part of $\dfrac{1}{x_1}$. In other words, we write

$$\frac{1}{x_1} = a_1 + x_2,$$

where a_1 is a non-negative integer and $0 \leqslant x_2 < 1$.

Repeating the process, we obtain

$$x = a_0 + x_1, \quad \text{where} \quad x_1 = x - a_0$$

$$\frac{1}{x_1} = a_1 + x_2, \quad \text{where} \quad x_2 = \frac{1}{x_1} - a_1$$

$$\frac{1}{x_2} = a_2 + x_3, \quad \text{where} \quad x_3 = \frac{1}{x_2} - a_2$$

etc.

Thus

$$x = a_0 + x_1$$

$$= a_0 + \frac{1}{(1/x_1)}$$

$$= a_0 + \frac{1}{a_1 + x_2} = a_0 + \cfrac{1}{a_1 + \cfrac{1}{(1/x_2)}}$$

$$= a_0 + \cfrac{1}{a_1 + \cfrac{1}{a_2 + x_3}} = a_0 + \cfrac{1}{a_1 + \cfrac{1}{a_2 + 1/(1/x_3)}}$$

etc.

These clumsy-looking things are rewritten so as to stay on the page as follows:

$$x = a_0 + \frac{1}{a_1 +} \; \frac{1}{a_2 +} \; \frac{1}{a_3 +} \; \frac{1}{a_4 +} \cdots$$

Notice that the $+$ signs stay in the denominator to indicate that we really have what is called a *continued fraction*, so-called because we continue to express the remainder at any stage in terms of another fraction. Notice also that if at any stage $x_n = 0$, the process simply stops.

Exercise 1

What kind of number would you say x was if its continued fraction expression terminated? (Consider some simple examples.) ■

A more interesting result (which we shall not prove) is the converse; that if x is rational, its continued fraction expansion must terminate somewhere.

Because of these two results, the position is very tidy; real numbers are rational (i.e. pseudo-rational) if and only if their continued fractions terminate. Hence a continued fraction expansion tells us not only the value of the number, but something of the nature of the number. This — at a somewhat higher level — is the kind of reason why continued fractions are still important in the theory of numbers.

Exercise 1
(2 minutes)

Discussion
* *

Particular Continued Fractions

Let us find the continued fraction expansion for $\frac{4}{5}$. By simple arithmetic, we have

$$\frac{4}{5} = \frac{1}{5/4}$$

$$= \frac{1}{1 + \dfrac{1}{4}}$$

$$= \frac{1}{1+} \; \frac{1}{4} \quad \text{in our special notation.}$$

But we could have written

$$\frac{4}{5} = \frac{1}{5/4}$$

$$= \frac{1}{1 + \dfrac{1}{3 + \dfrac{1}{1}}}$$

$$= \frac{1}{1+} \; \frac{1}{3+} \; \frac{1}{1}$$

Real numbers which are not rational are said to be irrational. Continued fractions for irrationals must be endless, for a terminating continued fraction represents a rational number.

Definition 1
* * *

Exercise 2

Exercise 2
(2 minutes)

(i) If

$$x = \frac{1}{1+} \; \frac{1}{1+} \; \frac{1}{1+} \cdots$$

show that

$$x = \frac{1}{1 + x};$$

hence find the value of x.

(ii) If

$$3\frac{14\,159}{100\,000} = a_0 + \frac{1}{a_1+} \; \frac{1}{a_2+} \; \frac{1}{a_3+} \cdots$$

find the values of a_0, a_1, a_2, a_3, and hence find four successive rational approximations to π (counting 3 as the first approximation). ■

Decimals

Discussion

Decimals to base 10 are already familiar to you; nevertheless it is worth looking at them in parallel with continued fractions.

The problem over the representation of a real number was to find a way of bringing in the only numerical symbols we had, namely $0, 1, 2, 3, \ldots$. What we did was to write

$$x = a_0 + x_1 \quad \text{where} \quad 0 < x_1 < 1.$$

As x_1 was less than 1, we could not use the natural numbers $1, 2, 3, \ldots$ directly to express its magnitude. But we noticed that $1 < \dfrac{1}{x_1}$, and that the natural numbers could then be involved in the value $\dfrac{1}{x_1}$.

(*continued on page 47*)

Solution 1   **Solution 1**

If

$$x = a_0 + \frac{1}{a_1},$$

then

$$x = \frac{a_0 a_1 + 1}{a_1}, \quad \text{which is rational.}$$

If

$$x = a_0 + \frac{1}{a_1 +} \frac{1}{a_2},$$

then

$$x = a_0 + \frac{1}{(a_1 a_2 + 1)/a_2}$$

$$= a_0 + \frac{a_2}{a_1 a_2 + 1}, \quad \text{which is rational.}$$

It should now be obvious that x must be a rational if its continued fraction terminates. ∎

Solution 2   **Solution 2**

(i) $\qquad x = \dfrac{1}{1+} \dfrac{1}{1+} \dfrac{1}{1+} \cdots$

$$= \frac{1}{1 + \dfrac{1}{1+} \dfrac{1}{1+} \dfrac{1}{1+} \cdots}$$

$$= \frac{1}{1 + x};$$

$$\therefore \quad x^2 + x - 1 = 0.$$

But by construction, x is positive; $\therefore$ x is the positive root of the above quadratic equation, that is

$$x = \frac{-1 + \sqrt{1 + 4}}{2}$$

$$= \frac{\sqrt{5} - 1}{2}$$

This number is the famous Greek "golden ratio".

(ii) $\qquad 3\dfrac{14\,159}{100\,000} = 3 + \dfrac{1}{100\,000/14\,159}$

$$= 3 + \frac{1}{7+} \frac{887}{14\,159}$$

$$= 3 + \frac{1}{7+} \frac{1}{14\,159/887}$$

$$= 3 + \frac{1}{7+} \frac{1}{15+} \frac{854}{887}$$

$$= 3 + \frac{1}{7+} \frac{1}{15+} \frac{1}{887/854}$$

$$= 3 + \frac{1}{7+} \frac{1}{15+} \frac{1}{1+} \cdots$$

$\therefore \quad a_0 = 3,$

$a_1 = 7,$

$a_2 = 15,$

$a_3 = 1.$

The first four approximations to $3\dfrac{14\,159}{100\,000}$ — which is itself a decimal approximation to π — are

$3,$

$$3 + \frac{1}{7} = \frac{22}{7},$$

$$3 + \frac{1}{7+} \frac{1}{15} = 3 + \frac{15}{106} = \frac{333}{106},$$

$$3 + \frac{1}{7+} \frac{1}{15+} \frac{1}{1} = 3 + \frac{16}{113} = \frac{355}{113}.$$

The first value has been used in classical times as an approximation to π; the second approximation to π is in frequent use today, and the fourth is commonly known. Is it a coincidence that all the approximations to π in common use are continued fraction approximations to π? No! There is a theorem which says that in some well-defined sense, continued fractions provide the best rational approximations to every positive real irrational number x. ■

(*continued from page 45*)

Inverting x_1 is not the only way of "inflating" x_1 so as to make the natural numbers relevant; we could multiply it by 10 (or, indeed, any other natural number: it is convenient to use the number base). Thus

$$\frac{22}{7} = 3 + \frac{1}{7}$$

and $10 \times \frac{1}{7}$ contains the whole number part 1. Thus

$$\frac{10}{7} = 1 + \frac{3}{7}.$$

Again, $10 \times \frac{3}{7} = \frac{30}{7} = 4 + \frac{2}{7}$ and so on. In this way, in a manner which is already familiar to you, we get the beginning of a decimal expansion

$$\frac{22}{7} = 3.14\ldots$$

(Of course, in decimals we can get zero in a decimal place.)

While decimals are less interesting than continued fractions, and depend on an arbitrary choice of base, they are far more convenient than continued fractions for most numerical work.

Exercise 3

(i) x is rational if and only if its continued fraction expansion terminates. Does the same remark apply to decimal expansions?

(ii) Do rationals possess alternative decimal expansions ? ■

Exercise 3
(2 minutes)

Solution 3

(i) No.

Some rationals have terminating decimals; thus

$$\frac{1}{8} = 0.125.$$

Some have endless decimals; thus

$$\frac{1}{7} = 0.142857 \ 142857 \ldots$$

But if a rational has an endless decimal, that decimal must recur. Conversely, a recurring decimal is equal to a rational. So x is rational if and only if its decimal representation either terminates or recurs.

(ii) Sometimes. Thus

$$\frac{1}{8} = 0.125 \quad \text{or} \quad 0.1249999\ldots$$

But

$$\frac{1}{7} = 0.142857 \ 142857 \ldots$$

and there is no alternative form.

If there are alternative forms, one form terminates and the other does not. Hence only rationals may possess alternative forms. This is another manifestation of ambiguity associated with the rationals (though not all rationals in this case). ■

34.4.5 Summary

What have we accomplished? Starting with a set of objects called the natural numbers, we have shown how to construct a set of objects which satisfies all the properties we normally associate with the intuitive real numbers. Since the objects we have constructed are concrete in the sense that they are based on mathematically understood operations rather than being part of our intuition, we call these objects *the* set of real numbers. We have seen that we can attach our familiar labels like $\frac{2}{3}$, $\frac{112}{375}$ to certain of the reals, and of course we can attach symbols like $\sqrt[3]{2}$, $\sqrt[5]{37}$, π, and e, etc. to certain others. Now we can return to our old manipulations and notations, satisfied that the real numbers are on a firm foundation, enhanced by an awareness of the greatest lower bound — least upper bound property.

One of the arguments that we used to justify the need for the real numbers involved the number line, and the apparent gaps in the rationals as labels for the points, as discovered by the Greeks. A very natural question would be, have we managed, by constructing the reals, to provide a real number as label for every point on the number line?

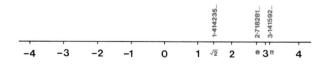

The answer is that it depends entirely on your definition of the number line. It turns out, however, that in the slightly rarefied atmosphere of axiomatics and logic, the concept of points on a line is itself far too imprecisely specified to base the number system on. In fact it is easiest, and most satisfactory to *define* the number line as a set of points in one-one correspondence with the reals! Hence the full name, the *real number line*.

Another argument used to justify the need for the reals involved the solution of certain equations. Can we now solve all equations in the reals? The answer is still No. The equation $x^2 + 1 = 0$ has no solution in the real numbers. As you know, we can proceed one step further to construct the complex numbers which then permits us to solve all polynomial equations with complex coefficients.

34.5 TRANSFINITE NUMBERS

In this section we shall briefly discuss extensions of the ideas of counting and ordering which were first actively studied by Georg Cantor.

34.5.1 Counting

Counting objects, to primitive people and children, often means putting them into one-one correspondence with fingers and thumbs. Thus, if, on counting objects in a set, we exhaust all five "fingers" of one hand, and we reach the middle finger of the other hand, we say there are 8 objects in the set. Moreover, in whatever order we take the objects, we always arrive at the same total number 8. We always exhaust the objects on reaching the 8th finger. With more than 10 objects, the method has to be adapted, but the principles remain the same; and one of the basic principles is that because of the one-one correspondence, the numbers of objects in the "fingers" set, and in the set being counted are equal. Noah knew all about this. He did not count the numbers of male and female animals going into the ark: he put males and females in one-one correspondence and thus knew he had equal numbers of each.

Georg Cantor
(Science Museum Library)

If neither set contains a finite number of elements, it is strictly meaningless to talk about the two sets having equal numbers of elements, for it is impossible to attach a number to either. What Cantor did in effect was to say that two sets could still be regarded as "equally numerous" if there existed a one-one correspondence between them.

We shall pursue these ideas, taking for our basic reference or "finger" set the set N of natural numbers. We shall begin by asking what appears to be a silly question. If E is the set of all even natural numbers, are E and N equally numerous? "Obviously not", you may say, "after all, E is a proper subset of N. Remove all the even numbers from N, and the odd numbers are left behind. There are obviously twice as many numbers as there are evens!" This is an understandable reaction; but look at the situation in terms of one-one correspondences. If you pair off — or match — the number $2n$ from N with the number $2n$ from E, then plainly you exhaust E without even beginning on the odd numbers in N. But you do not have to set up the correspondence in this way; you can match n from N with $2n$ from E, and then it is clear that there *can* be a one-one correspondence between N and E. It follows that N and E are equally numerous.

Example 1

Example 1

We shall show that the set of primes, P, and N are equally numerous.

We first use a proof by contradiction to show that there is no "last" prime.

Suppose that there is a last prime; let it be p_n. Taking

$$N = p_1 p_2 \cdots p_n + 1,$$

N has a prime factor, since $p_n < N$ and p_n is the last prime.

But the only prime numbers available are $p_1, p_2, \ldots, p_n$. Therefore there will be some p_i dividing N. But p_i divides $p_1 p_2 \cdots p_n = N - 1$. If p_i divides both N and $N - 1$, it must divide $N - (N - 1) = 1$. But this is impossible, as $p_i \neq 1$. Therefore our supposition is false, and there is no last prime.

If p_n is the nth prime, we match n to p_n; this sets up a one-one correspondence between N and P. Therefore N and P are equally numerous. ∎

34.5.2 The Rationals Q^+

Even if you are now reconciled to E and N being equally numerous, you must surely expect Q^+ to be more numerous than N; that is, you must expect it to be impossible to match N to Q^+. Whole numbers appear as isolated points on the number line, and between any two there are infinitely many rationals. A further difficulty is that there is no first positive rational. It seems impossible even to start the matching process. Yet if we drop any attempt to preserve ordering according to magnitude, we can succeed.

Matching the rationals to the natural numbers means in effect arranging them in a line so that there is a first rational (which is matched to 1) followed by a second (which is matched to 2) and so forth. We shall do this, but the other way round; that is, we shall set out the rationals in an infinite square lattice, and then weave a line through them.

We take the positive quadrant of Cartesian co-ordinates, and place the rational $\frac{p}{q}$ at the point (p, q). We obtain

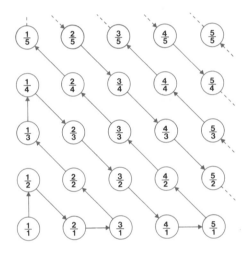

It is obvious that the red line meets every rational; in fact it meets some rationals many times over (e.g. it meets $\frac{1}{2}$ in the forms $\frac{1}{2}, \frac{2}{4}, \frac{3}{6}, \ldots$). Hence the rationals are matched to the natural numbers, so N and Q^+ are equally numerous.

34.5.3 The Reals in $]0, 1[$

Are *all* infinite sets equally numerous?

We shall examine this question in terms of the natural numbers, and the reals in the interval $]0, 1[$. Suppose that a matching has been set up, and that the whole number n matches to the real number x_n, where $0 < x_n < 1$. If we express all these reals in terms of endless binary "decimals", we get, say:

$$x_1 = 0.1000011\ldots$$
$$x_2 = 0.1111010\ldots$$
$$x_3 = 0.0110100\ldots$$
$$x_4 = 0.1010100\ldots$$
$$\vdots$$

In the complete matching, every real number occurs somewhere. Therefore the real number

$$y = 0.0001 \ldots$$

occurs somewhere in the complete table. But y has been chosen to differ from x_1 in its first "decimal" place, and from x_2 in its second "decimal" place, and so on. Therefore y is *different* from *all* the x's; therefore y is not matched to any n. However we shuffle things around, there will always be some y which is left out of the matching.

At last therefore we have come across a class which is so numerous that it cannot be matched with N. In other words, (and very loosely) not all infinities are equal. This being so, we have to distinguish these infinities, or as we now prefer to call them, *transfinite numbers*. The transfinite number associated with the set N is denoted by $\aleph_0$ (aleph nought), and the transfinite number associated with the set R is denoted by c (c for continuum). Whether there are other transfinite numbers, and in particular whether there are transfinite numbers between $\aleph_0$ and c are deep questions, not all of which have yet been answered.

Unit No.		Title of Text
1		Functions
2		Errors and Accuracy
3		Operations and Morphisms
4		Finite Differences
5	NO TEXT	
6		Inequalities
7		Sequences and Limits I
8		Computing I
9		Integration I
10	NO TEXT	
11		Logic I — Boolean Algebra
12		Differentiation I
13		Integration II
14		Sequences and Limits II
15		Differentiation II
16		Probability and Statistics I
17		Logic II — Proof
18		Probability and Statistics II
19		Relations
20		Computing II
21		Probability and Statistics III
22		Linear Algebra I
23		Linear Algebra II
24		Differential Equations I
25	NO TEXT	
26		Linear Algebra III
27		Complex Numbers I
28		Linear Algebra IV
29		Complex Numbers II
30		Groups I
31		Differential Equations II
32	NO TEXT	
33		Groups II
34		Number Systems
35		Topology
36		Mathematical Structures